Preface

The content of this book provides 'stories for the end of life'. These have been written as part of a partnership project between the Strategic Health Authority NHS West Midlands, Bridges Support Service and the Arts Council.

We had a project team made up of ourselves (Pauline and Manjula) and a professional story-teller, Maria Whatton. Both Maria and Manjula worked together with local people recruited from Sandwell and Birmingham communities to participate in this work.

This book is a way of giving the stories back to all those who contributed - a treasure to keep. It is a way of saying thank you for your munificent* contribution.

We hope the introduction to and the contents of this book will help make sense of why a book such as this is needed in the twenty-first century and that such stories can help us to travel our life journey in more prepared ways.

Pauline Smith End of Life Care Lead - NHS West Midlands
Manjula Patel Manager - Bridges Support Service

*From the Latin word *munus*, which means gift.

Bridges Support Service

Bridges is a supportive care service supporting people living with cancer and palliative care needs in Sandwell and parts of Birmingham. The service is a bridge to access services from health, social and community organisations and where there are gaps Bridges provides appropriate support. Bridges is managed by Murray Hall Community Trust, a registered charity. (www.murrayhall.co.uk)

The development of the Bridges service has intrinsically been linked to patients and carers' stories. Bridges has also pioneered 'Narrative Based Assessments' to enable the service to provide tailored support based on the patient's story.

More about the Project

To find out more about the project and have the opportunity to explore some additional resources visit the Wellbeing in Dying web site:

www.wellbeingindying.org.uk

The First Primrose

Stories for Wellbeing at the End of Life

Edited by Maria Whatton

Contents

First published 2008

Murray Hall Community Trust
Neptune Health Park
Sedgley Road West
Tipton
West Midlands
DY4 8LU

Produced by Jovian Productions Ltd.
www.jovianproductions.co.uk

Introduction

Storytelling is an ancient art form that offers a contribution to the development and sustaining of a collective wisdom. The stories in this book offer you a way of becoming more familiar with the subject matter of dying and death. We hope it facilitates your becoming more empowered to embrace your own experiences, or those close to you. This is about reconnecting with what we know but have forgotten.

In these stories there are witnesses to death as well as those who have had a taste of their own mortality. By telling these stories we are trying to put something in place for future generations that may not have the same support systems as in the past.

Maria Whatton, storyteller and writer, worked alongside Manjula Patel over a period of nine months with participants from the local area to help them tell and formalise the stories you will find in this collection. Maria shared myths, legends and folk tales from around the world with the participants. Participants in turn related their first hand encounters with dying, death and mortality.

You will also find a story called The First Primrose, which is a newly written piece by Maria. It speaks in the language of poetry and metaphor encapsulating the main themes the writer found in the participants' stories. 'The First Primrose' is a direct response to participants' experiences.

Context for the Book

In the twenty-first century what do we draw on to make sense of the end of life? How do we see clearly what is right in front of us? The answers to these questions will either be enhanced or made worse by our expectations. What do we as individuals bring to the table in terms of our religious beliefs, spiritual beliefs, culture, traditions and experiences?

We will all die. The manner of dying and death is different for us today as compared to say a century ago. In the western world death is now mostly viewed under a medical lens. There have been numerous medical developments that allow us to recover from situations where previously death would have been an expected outcome. We live longer, but these developments also make the fine line between living and death difficult. Now it is possible for body parts to be replaced, vital organs such as heart and liver, which only fifty years ago may have seemed impossible. Renewal is now part of our psyche. Prior to these groundbreaking advancements there would have been certain death. Faced with a situation such as this many questions need to be answered: will this replacement benefit my life or do I come to terms with my body dying? Will this give life quality or life longevity? Is getting both achievable? Will it actually work? All these things come into play.

The NHS is geared towards the curative mode, so it doesn't always know how to help us differentiate between life and death. For some there are benefits, for others there aren't. The notion of a natural death is difficult to embody.

It is time for the public to think about, and to tussle with, these difficult issues, because we need to be part of how we die well. Death for us all is inevitable and dying and death as a human being is more than our medical state.

Perhaps it is time that we begin to regard our medical care for the end of life in the same way that we now look at the beginning of life - childbirth. It is now commonplace for women to plan the birth of a child right down to the music that they want played during labour. Birth plans include an ideal scenario and a back up plan for if things go differently, which may require hospitalisation.

Our communities have lost some of the knowledge and wisdom for dealing with dying and death. We seem to have become disconnected and forgotten how to accept that death and dying is a natural part of life. We have forgotten what to do, how to be engaged and how to lead. It is a paradox, a dialogue of conflicting forces: on the one hand we know that ultimately we're going to die, on the other we are so intrinsically involved in the process of living that it is difficult to engage with the idea of life ending.

We hope that these stories will be part of our regaining our connection to our inner and collective wisdom about dying and death.

Pauline Smith
End of Life Care Lead NHS West Midlands

The Power of Stories

In an old Kazakhstan folk tale, Korkut dreams that Death is searching for him. When he wakes up he gallops away as fast as he can on his chestnut horse. Wherever he turns graves are being dug for him. It seems even nature itself cannot help him. Eventually Korkut's horse becomes so exhausted he dies. Korkut shapes a musical instrument from a nearby tree and uses the hair from his horse's tail to make a bow. He begins to sing. He enchants everyone who stops and listens, even Death. After a while Korkut is ready. He hands his musical instrument to the people and gives himself to Death. When the people play the instrument and sing Korkut's stories Korkut and his horse live on - for in the realm of stories there is no death.

This ancient tale sums up for me the potency of the stories told to me during this project. I was privileged to hear them told vividly by each participant. In these accounts those who have died and the emotions of the teller are real and current. Each life journey is described with unflinching honesty, which gives us (the listeners/readers) a tremendous document of end of life experience at the beginning of the twenty-first century. Each story cannot fail to touch your heart. As a teller of myths, legends and folktales I was consistently aware of the commonalities that ran through all of our stories: the human condition, unfathomable questions, wisdom, powerful emotions and the tenacity of the human spirit. I hope you get as much out of reading these stories as I did listening to them.

Maria Whatton
Storyteller and Writer

The First Primrose

by Maria Whatton

Long before it happened the seasons told the story first.

They listened, but did not hear the wisdom of nature's interminable cycle as we all do and we all don't: the first primrose of spring, the hot blue sea of summer, the golden leaves of autumn and the last glistening star of winter.

High in the arms of the tree two children, Mischa and Stephan, brother and sister, sang songs and watched dappled leaf shadows trail down into the world below. From their branch thrones they sat and swayed making pictures out of the clouds so close they felt they could reach out and touch them. This was their tree, a place that they could escape to. They would climb high and watch the rest of the village scurry like ants about their daily chores.

"I'll always be your friend" said Stephan.
"And I will always be here for you singing songs" Mischa laughed.
They twittered their imaginings and dreams to each other amongst the flock of birds that made their home in the knotty resting places of the tree's branches. They sat in the tree as the seasons changed. Luscious blossom gave way to ripened fruit. Yellow leaves glowed in the September sun before falling to the ground revealing the naked branches of winter.

Mischa and Stephan were hardly apart. Together they discovered the first primrose of each new spring. In summer they stitched the hottest, bluest sea with their arms. Each autumn they raked up a treasure of golden leaves from the garden, and in winter they watched the last glistening star before it faded into the first frost filled morning of spring.

The children grew up. Now brother and sister lived in their own cottage on the far side of the village in the shadow of their favourite tree. They busied themselves with the pleasures and toils of their daily life. Mischa baked bread in the morning; Stephan stoked the last embers of the fire at night. They glided through their daily routines like a hot knife through butter. Together, as they worked, they sang songs like birds set free.

When Stephan fell in love with a girl from the next village Mischa was overjoyed and welcomed her like a sister to their home. Now the two women cooked together, fetched water together and tended the garden.

Before long Stephan and his wife had two dear little girls. The cottage was filled with the exuberance of childhood. When Stephan and his wife dozed exhausted at the end of a hard day's work Aunt Mischa would snuggle up with the children next to the fire watching the amber coals glow and sing them soothing songs that rose and twisted into the air like the fragrant wood smoke curving up inside the chimney.

One winter night a great storm awoke them. A blizzard raged. All evening the wind whipped around the cottage, rattling the windows and tugging at the roof tiles. All night long a tree branch knocked unremittingly against Stephan's bedroom window like an insistent guest demanding to come in. That night nobody slept well in their beds. The children woke up their aunt and deep into the night she held them close and sang them lullabies by candlelight.

The next morning as Stephan cleared the debris outside the house picking up stray branches, clods of earth and odd tiles that had speared themselves into the soft earth, he bent down to pick up what he thought was a piece of broken bark. To his astonishment he realised he had found a tiny box no bigger than a nut. On the sides were intricate shapes but the box was so small he could not make out what they were. As he held the box in his hand a cold shiver of wind wrapped itself around him like a noose. For a moment the evil wind whipped away his breath. Stephan tried to open the box jamming his thumbnail at the edge of the tiny lid. It refused to open. He figured it was big enough to house a ring or a jewel, although equally he thought it could be something more sinister: a severed fingertip, perhaps, a poisonous blade. The lid would not shift no matter how hard he tried. He thought about telling his wife and his sister what he had found, but the box seemed so harmless he simply stored it in his pocket and thought nothing more of it.

The storm had created such havoc there was much to do and much to occupy them. The crops had been ripped out by their roots. The fence looked as though a giant had trampled it and the barn door swung off its hinges like a broken tooth. There was planting to be done, mending and repairing. Stephan was so busy he did not pay much attention to the box rubbing against his skin. Winter passed and so too spring. Stephan did not notice too much the box weighing a little heavier in the pocket of his overalls.

One fine summer morning he pulled it out and looked at it. It was now the size of a small bird. He decided to get rid of it and throw it away with the waste, but when he tried he couldn't. It stuck fast to his hand. He showed his wife who tried to ease it away from his skin with ointment. She tried to chip away at it with a knife. Nothing happened. It stayed there solid as rock. Mischa came and she tried too, but nothing seemed to be able to budge the box that was now a fixed attachment to Stephan's body.

"Try to sleep tonight and we will see what we can do in the morning" said Mischa not wanting to show her worry. "I'm sure we'll think of something".

So that night Stephan went to bed and tried to sleep. Something strange was happening to him and he did not know what to do. From outside the bedroom window he could see the shape of the tree and he remembered the songs and dreams of his childhood. The tree whispered Mischa's words "I will always be here for you singing songs" and with that he fell into a deep sleep.

When he woke in the morning his hand weighed heavy under the sheets. The box had grown once again. Now it was the size of an axe head. Something had to be done. He was scared. As Stephan's children played outside in the branches of the tree, as he and Mischa had once done, he looked to his sister and his wife for help.

"We must seek out the wise woman, and act on her advice" said Mischa. "The children will be safe here with their mother and the new crops will need to be nurtured and harvested. I will go with you and we will take the journey together".

So it was agreed. Stephan kissed his wife and held his children. He made sure there was enough for them to eat and the fields were tilled, then he and Mischa left seeking the hermitage of the wise woman.

"It is not for me to force your feet along any one path" she said, "but burdens such as this are common". The wise woman surveyed the pale stones in her obsidian cave as though she was looking for truth in the darkness. "Only when you find the first primrose of spring will you know that your journey is done. Now leave me. I can help you no more".

"The first primrose of spring?" whispered Stephan to his sister as they left the cave, "but we are only at the beginning of summer". "Then we will have to search" said Mischa. She looked around. "There seems to be only one path" she said. All the other paths were overgrown with briars or left in disrepair. They were forgotten roads. "Come!" she said and began to lead him along a sun filled path high into the mountains.

As they walked Mischa helped her brother by singing favourite songs. She tried to lift his spirits but she could see her brother was in pain. He held his burdened hand. There was a shimmer of sweat on his brow. "Mischa, this road is dusty and stony and I can see nothing ahead of us. Perhaps we should head back?"

"Do not worry" Mischa smiled. "I am at your side and tonight I promise you, we will sleep in the palace of a thousand diamonds". And Mischa kept her word. That night as darkness fell she unfurled the blankets she had packed and laid them on the ground. She made a fire to keep her brother warm. As Stephan lay in his makeshift bed he looked up into the black velvety night sky studded with stars and smiled gently to himself. This was a magnificent palace indeed.

The next morning brother and sister set off once again. It was not long before they found themselves in a thick and tangled forest. The path was now almost impossible to follow. Many times they trudged on and on for hours only to discover that they were back in the same spot.

Stephan had to stop and rest. During the night the box had mysteriously relocated itself from Stephan's hand onto his back. His hands were free but his body was bent to try and accommodate its weight. He staggered on. By nightfall they were no further forwards. Mischa could feel her heart race with fear. There were poisonous snakes in the forest and fierce creatures. She began to call for help. Her voice echoed helplessly around the tops of the pitiless trees. Fear crept around her like a cloak of ice. There was nobody around to help them. She was cold, lost and alone.

Mischa looked at her brother resting awkwardly against the butt of a gigantic tree. She could hear his pained breath. Her heart swelled with compassion. She had no choice but to find a way out. Once more she called out. When there was no reply she sat down on a bed of leaves and began to think about retracing the path they had begun. Just then she heard a rustle of leaves. At first she thought it might be a fierce beast smelling out their blood and she rushed to protect her brother, but then she saw a hooded figure moving towards her. She ran towards him and stopped. An emaciated man with a kind face stood before her. "I heard your cries" he said. "I have come to help".

That night they slept in the hermit's cave. He had lived at the edge of the forest for many years. When he heard Mischa's cries he had slowly made his way towards her. "We are lost" said Mischa as she shared the simple meal that the hermit prepared for them. "Where do we go to next?" "Not far from here there is a valley" said the hermit. "I can direct you. There you will meet with other travellers like yourselves". And so the next day the hermit guided them out of the tangled woods and pointed towards a valley. Stephan and Mischa thanked him for his kindness and as the sun rose they went on their way.

As they got closer they could hear the voices of hundreds of people milling around or resting in the valley below. As they arrived, for the first time Stephan saw other people in the same predicament as himself. Some were carrying small boxes, others were weighed down like Stephan. Mischa noticed that there were people like her too and within a short space of time brother and sister were sitting and conversing with the others like old friends.

As they sat and talked a great bird shaped cloud cast its shadow across the crowds. Mischa watched as the cloud transformed into a golden eagle that intermittently flew then landed amongst the crowds of people. As the day went on the eagle circled closer towards them. Mischa noticed that some people no longer carried boxes and were happily making their way out of the valley; others still looked weak and in pain and some people seemed to have disappeared from sight. Mischa leaned towards a woman who was caring for her father. "Who is this creature?" she asked. "The golden eagle of limited knowledge. If you wish him to, he will tell you the truth as far as he knows it" the woman replied before returning to mop the old man's brow. Mischa wanted to know. She sat and waited.

At last the eagle perched on a rock close to Mischa. Stephan had fallen into an exhausted sleep. Mischa left her seat beside her brother and joined the kindly looking eagle on the rock. "Tell me! What shall I do to help my brother?" she demanded. The eagle looked directly at her. His feathers ruffled in the gentle breeze. "The truth is, your brother has almost finished his journey. Soon the box will obliterate him. What you can do for your brother is what you are already doing". With that he flapped his wings and flew away.

That night Mischa looked at the stars as though somewhere among them she might find hope. With the first light she knew they would have to leave this place. There was no point staying here any longer.

"But I didn't get to speak with the eagle" said Stephan. They were now four hours walk away from the valley. Mischa helped her weakened brother through the dusty bowl of a landscape that lay ahead of them. "Perhaps the eagle could have helped me" Stephan said. "Perhaps he didn't spend time with me because I will be better soon. Perhaps by this time next month I will be reaping the crops as I always do and everything will be the same as it always was". Now the brother and sister were standing high up at the entrance to a shady crevasse. Mischa stopped and helped her brother sit inside to protect him from the gritty sands swirling around them. "Stephan, while you slept I conversed with the eagle" she said tenderly. "The box is not going to disappear. You will never return to your former self". She held out her hand to him. He took it and held it close to his face. For a few moments he was silent and then he spoke. "Then I want to go home" he said.

As he slept that night Mischa wandered back to the top of the dusty bowl of earth. The moon looked down at her mockingly. She wanted to rip it out of the sky and tear it into tiny shreds. She kicked the dust beneath her feet and her body raged with injustice. Her brother didn't deserve this. What harm had he ever done to anyone? He had always done the best he could for his family, his land and his friends. Then suddenly, as though a gale had pushed her forward she fell to her knees. She cried to the mountains that surrounded her. "How am I expected to go on without him?" her voice echoed in the darkness. Then she began to weep. Great hot salty tears washed down her face. They fell and splashed in rivulets around her. Her tears ran down and began to fill the bowl carved in the earth. She wept and wept until her tears were raging waves around her. She had wept a lake of tears and she was lost in its centre. She was about to sink and drown. Madly she beat her arms and kicked her feet. She struggled to catch her breath. Then as she began to get into her rhythm she remembered the many summers where she and her brother had splashed through the sea with joy and her tearful lake soothed her. Gracefully she moved through it and reached the other side. She was exhausted and drenched but she knew she was ready to make the next part of the journey.

Ahead of them were green fields speckled with yellow buttercups. Stephan was now so burdened by the cumbersome box across his shoulders Mischa had summoned all her strength to carry him.

From here she could see their tree in the distance. It was beginning to shed its blossom and the pale petals drifted like snow towards them. Mischa sang softly to her brother. His bones felt light and as delicate as china.

"I will always be your friend" whispered Stephan as he gasped for breath. "And I will always be here for you singing songs" replied Mischa.

It was February and a delicate frost coated the roof of the little cottage. The tree glinted and twinkled next to the sparkling garden.

"I'm sorry girls it's too cold to go and climb the tree today" scolded their mother as Rosa and Lily stared out of their father's bedroom window. Aunt Mischa was sitting next to her brother's bed in the rocking chair. Months had passed since she had carried him home. Stephan, as pale as the frost, managed to take a sip of water from the cup that his wife held to his lips. "Dadda" cried Rosa the eldest jabbing her finger at the windowpane "Guess what I can see?"

There at the foot of the tree poking its head from the earth the first primrose had emerged fluttering like a white moth amongst the frozen blades of grass. "Take me to it" said Stephan. He strained his head towards the window.

Stephan's wife and Aunt Mischa carried him out into the garden. "It's so pretty" sighed Rosa as they studied it. A light spray of frost fell from the tree and sprinkled across the curves of the leaves. Then something extraordinary began to happen. The box began to grow. The coarse, weird patterns on all four sides were changing. It was as though an invisible artist was carving exquisite details into the wood.

Stephan's fragile body disappeared into the earth as quickly as an airborne salmon back into a river. The box glowed amidst the sparkling frost and Mischa saw each design in perfect lucidity. There, engraved on the four sides, were the seasons of Stephan's life: the first primrose of spring, the hot blue sea of summer, the golden leaves of autumn and the last glistening star of winter. It was at that moment that Mischa understood the wisdom of the first primrose: everything changes, everything passes and now she knew for sure that what had happened to her brother was as natural as the seasons themselves. Stephan's wife held her daughters' hands and took them inside.

Mischa stood for a while in the garden staring at the box. She studied the engravings on its surface and without a second thought ran her hand across the lines and curves of the design. An electric spark ran through her fingertips and the box lid burst open. A whirlwind of glittering words rushed into the air. Mischa breathed in and the words fell in a rush into her mouth. When she looked again the box had disappeared.

When Aunt Mischa sat by the fireside telling Stephan's daughters stories her words glittered and sparkled. The box had given her a treasure just as it had taken away her beloved brother. Now she could pass on the legacy of stories from her brother's life. Now she knew that at some point his story would become her own story for it is the story of all human kind.

The Man

Tony's story told by Barbara

*"You are my garden
my world and my sky"*

A couple of months before Tony was diagnosed he kept going to see the doctor. He thought there was something wrong with his tongue. The doctor kept telling him he had tonsillitis. In the end he said "I'm going to ask for a referral".

He was sent to the hospital. He said "Mom, I want you there with me". When he came out he said "I've got cancer". I started crying.

When we went back the doctor said to Tony "you can have an operation or chemotherapy. If you have chemo you may have six months, if you have the operation you could have up to five or six years". Tony said to me "what'll I do Mom?" and I said "Tony, don't put that on me". The operation entailed cutting down under his chin and throat and putting a vein out of his arm under his tongue. He decided to have the operation.

Four days later he was down in the operating theatre. The first operation lasted seven and a half hours. That wasn't totally successful, so he had to have another, which was another seven and a half hours. It took him five hours to recover. There were pipes coming out of him. He was in critical care for a month. We nearly lost him. He had a heart attack and a stroke. You could only kiss him on one arm. After a month they pulled him up in bed and he winked one eye. We all applauded.

Tony had no saliva after the first cancer. He couldn't talk. I would be his voice. I'd talk for him. The first time he managed to say thank you I was so happy. On one occasion the man in the next bed to Tony told me Tony couldn't say yes to a cup of tea, so he had to wait for me to come and visit so he could have a drink.

He came home and his girlfriend looked after him for six months then she walked out on him. About a year later Tony said "Mom, I think I've got a lump in my leg. He went to the hospital. "I'm sorry" they said "you've got cancer in your leg". They put a rod in his leg from his knee. He walked on sticks. Another year passed and Tony found another lump in his leg so he had to go into another hospital. They had to put a stainless steel new hip in. He had

120 staples. He never complained.

I used to drive with Tony. He'd had a heart attack and a stroke. I'd keep my legs and arms crossed. "Oh well, if we crash, we go together" I'd think. He drove to all his hospital appointments.

I had a stair lift put in. "Mom" he said "I don't ever want to be on my own again". I said to him "you won't ever be on your own again my lad". For five and a half years from then on I slept on his settee. I used to get cramp in my leg but it didn't bother me. I got to like sleeping on the couch after a bit.

I had him a nice shower and bathroom put in.

The man from the council came. "Has he got any savings?" he said. "He hasn't worked for thirteen years. He's had a serious car accident and he's got cancer" I said. "My son could be dead in four months".

I had to wash him the best way I could.

My Tony had thirty-seven lots of radiotherapy mostly on his neck. It burned him deep into his neck.

He had twelve lots on his leg.

They'd put X marks on him and still cheerfully he'd say "look Mom, another tattoo". Even though he was on Morphine he'd still drive to the hospital.

Even when he was ill my son fetched the old man Patrick's medication from the chemists. He was very ill himself. I'd go to the hospital every day to see Tony. Tony went from seventeen stone to ten stone. He was so ill.

Manjula (from Bridges) was my best friend when I was going through it all. What helped was she'd phone and see me and we'd just talk.

The doctor hadn't seen Tony for nineteen days before he died. To release the death certificate they were talking about having to do an autopsy. "No. My lad's been cut up enough" I said.

The Human Rights woman helped me fill in a form for a carer's allowance. The carer from Hospice at Home got him £200 for a new wardrobe because he had lost so much weight and she also got him a microwave. That really helped.

He couldn't help it but he couldn't go to the toilet for nine days then it would go everywhere. We'd laugh so much. 'Plop plops' we'd call it. Tony would have his games and his telly and sometimes he'd just stare. He was his own person. He was just like that.

When Tony died he was watching telly. "Go and have a lie down Mother" he kept saying. Bert my husband said "I'll look after him". I remember hearing "Barb, Barb, Tony's gone" and I thought "where's he gone?"

There was blood everywhere. I stopped with him after. I wanted to have him to myself. I wanted everyone to go.

He went quickly in the end and not from cancer. The undertaker cleaned up. There was so much blood. He said, "don't worry about anything like that darling". They were wonderful. My comfort is that he is with my dad.

I'd clean Tony's ears with toilet roll. He'd say "give that here!" and he'd get stuff out I couldn't. We used to laugh about it. I'd sometimes change his sheets twice a night. He wouldn't let anyone clean him except for me.

He only wanted me to touch him. When he had to have a pipe in his stomach he had to have seven stitches around it. One day I looked over the nurse's shoulder. I said "it's gone septic". We had to take him to hospital. All the stitches had to be taken out.

Tony was in that much pain when the cancer came on his liver. His brother phoned for an ambulance. I came from the pub. I was there within minutes. Tony was lying on his side. The ambulance man kept saying he had to move him but he was in so much pain I stopped them. "When he's ready I'll tell you" I said. I gave him four lots of Diamorphine and then he was able to go. I was really upset about it. After a while they said they'd have to operate to see what was wrong with him. Tony squeezed the doctor's arm and said "please get rid of the pain for me".

The consultant was nice. "He's got cancer on the liver" he said. I started to cry but I never cried in front of Tony. I knew if I cried he would. I waited for two whole weeks for him to tell my son. When that doctor came I knew what he was going to say to Tony. The Macmillan nurse knew too and she came and held my hand.

Tony went from seventeen stone to ten stone to seven stone.

The doctor broke the news to Tony and Tony just shrugged. I knew when the doctors were telling Tony that it was too tiring for him to travel to the hospitals that there wasn't much more they could do for him. When he went to the toilet and it went everywhere I knew it was his body clearing out before he died. He never complained, not even at the end.

My son was 'THE MAN'. Tony was a wonderful man.

Tony is buried with my dad. What gives me a bit of comfort is knowing they're together. On the grave it says: 'Safe in the arms of Grandad'. Sometimes I see Tony and my dad together in a meadow full of flowers sitting on a bench.

Fishing with Tony

Bert's story told by Barbara

*"I now hold the key to my heart
where all our memories are locked away."*

I married Bert on 2nd November, 1963. He was a tall handsome man with auburn wavy hair. My husband was very caring, loving and patient. He was a very good working man and a wonderful loving father and grandad.

Bert started feeling unwell in 1981. He tried to keep up with his job but in 1983 his ulcers burst. He was very poorly and went down to six stone. Gradually he started to get a lot stronger and put weight back on. At last he got up to nine stone. We just carried on until 1995; Bert had a heart attack, which left him with angina. He also suffered asthma, spondylitis and arthritis. Bert attended hospital and went to the doctors. He was in hospital quite a lot. Sometimes I had to telephone an ambulance twice in one week.

Bert tried not to let his illnesses get him down. He was always the life and soul and always smiling especially when our son Tony took him fishing. Tony died May 8th 2006 and I've told Tony's story.

I had to phone an ambulance on 4th December, 2007. Bert had been up all night. The hospital did a lot of tests and X-rays. Bert's stomach was massive but they said not to worry. After four hours they sent us home. "Come on, we will have a taxi" I said. "No, we'll go on the bus" Bert said. Bert ran for the bus. "You can go on, Barb. You'll be cold" Bert said as we were going up the road to our house. Bert said he wanted to be sick. "No, I'll wait for you" I said.

When we got home I made Bert a drink. He said "Barb, I'm going to lie down". He was not upstairs more than two minutes. When he came down he was not the same man that had gone upstairs. Bert slumped on the settee and said "Barb, I'm going down". I will never, ever forget my husband's face. It was not my husband. "You're going nowhere. You said you would never leave me" I shouted. "Love me, Barb" Bert said. I said "I do love you" and gave him a kiss. I said, "I'll phone the ambulance back". "Don't lose me down, Barb" Bert said.

I went back in the hall to phone and Bert was right behind me. I don't know how he got there. He was leaning on me.

I couldn't hold him. He was a big man. I helped him to sit on the bottom step of the stairs. I held his hands and he fell back looking at me while I phoned. When I looked back at Bert his eyes were shut. "Don't leave me sweetheart!" I shouted, but I knew Bert had gone. The ambulance men worked hard on him but it was no good. I told Bert to go to the light where our son Tony would be waiting for him. I imagine Bert and Tony together now fishing and enjoying the sun.

The emptiness you feel after losing the love of your life is overwhelming. It's so lonely even in a room full of people. God bless you, my sweetheart.

Aeroplanes in the Sky

Geoff's story told by Sheila

"Your love of the long light evenings, the days we spent in the open air
Enjoying our picnics and flying your planes."

Geoff had got so he couldn't swallow. It caused him pain. The doctor referred him to the hospital. Unfortunately, he was diagnosed with cancer of the oesophagus. They organised for him to go to the hospital for radiotherapy. They took him every day for a week but they wouldn't let me go because of the transport situation. After a while they started chemotherapy. It knocked him about terrible. He ended up in hospital having to have transfusions.

In the November we had to go to outpatients. "It's knocking you about so much we'll give you a break from it" the Specialist said. I held back. "Does that mean there's no more you can do for him?" I said when Geoff left the room. "Yes" was the reply. Geoff didn't know this. I kept it to myself. He came home for Christmas. I promised him I'd keep him at home. He seemed to pick up and he was alive for the birth of his grandson at New Year.

In February I knew there'd be a right time to tell him. It was very hard to keep the secret but I didn't want to spoil Christmas or the news of the baby's birth. I coped well enough. When I did tell him he accepted it. "When I'm better..." he kept saying and I said "I'm sorry, you're not going to get better".

We'd always been so close. We'd been together for fifty years. We became even closer during that time because we could make plans.

Geoff had been my carer for so long. The roles reversed and I became his carer. I had help from Bridges, Crossroads, and the district nurses. It was better because I could make plans about how I was going to manage. I assured him I'd be all right. I know Geoff worried a lot about it because since then I've found out that's why my neighbour comes twice a week to do my shopping. It's because he promised Geoff. My daughter does my big shop, but it's nice to know he organised it and they talked about it. Geoff always insisted I had a night out. Our neighbour would sit with him so they must have talked about it then.

The chemo classes during Geoff's treatment were nice. They were almost like a party. People would take sandwiches and sweets. They'd chat to each other. The day I was told about

Geoff we went back to the ward. People were waiting for chemo. I had to tell them we wouldn't be coming again. I think I knew then.

I thank God for the six months we got. I didn't think we were going to get them. He was always cheerful even when he was in hospital and they moved him from one ward to another.

I noticed one day there was blood on the floor. Geoff's big toe was bleeding from under the nail. I got a tissue and mopped it. I called the nurse. They put a dressing on it. The toe gradually went black. It could have been gangrene. It was shrivelling. He also got an ulcer on his leg. He came out in terrible blotches – like bruises. They were on his hands and his neck. I don't know what that was.

The district nurses were marvellous and provided me with night sitters. In the June – the last two weeks – you could see he was really going down. In the last few days the district nurse said it wouldn't be long.

On Monday our daughter stayed all night with her dad. The next night the other two girls came but I don't know whether Geoff knew they were there. My son was just around the corner so he could be got quick.

The sitter insisted we went to bed. Just after 5 am in the morning she came and said "he's gone". He had lifted up his arms in the air. We were convinced he had gone into his mother's arms. She had come for him.

Everyone rushed downstairs but I had to wait for my lift. When I got there – it wasn't Geoff, it was just his body.

My nephew got married on the day Geoff died. I shall never forget his wedding anniversary.

The only things that didn't change were his hands. Even in his coffin he had the most wonderful hands. At school Geoff had got prizes for drawing and he had drawn his own hands. I can't find that drawing. I've put it somewhere safe.

If they had not let him come home he would not have lived to New Year.

We were given a clock as a twenty-fifth wedding anniversary present from our children. I stopped it because its chimes were disturbing Geoff when he was ill. I stopped it at five past seven. It was strange because that was the exact time Geoff died.

I was sixteen when I met Geoff. I'd had rheumatic fever. I used to wear leg irons. I was going to a dance that night and I did not want them creaking everywhere so I left them off. That night I met him. I never wore them again.

My lasting thoughts about Geoff are about everyone saying what a nice man he was.

The Girl and the Red Fox

Doreen's story

"It's 50/50 whether I survive this time or not.
Some people can't talk about it. I can."

For years I was a nurse and I'd be with people who'd had heart attacks - they'd be full of regrets. That must be a horrible way to die so I think of myself as very fortunate.

The local funeral director is all paid for and organised.

The vicar came and he said I could have one piece of music of my choice. I come from Lancashire. I want Gracie Fields 'At the End of the Day'. You might think it's irrelevant. I don't. I don't want anything dirgey, no funeral music. I used to do lots of ballet dancing and 'Coppelia' was my favourite. When the church is emptying I want the waltz from that. I've paid for the food for everyone at the church hall, but only all my family will go to the crem. I've been very fortunate.

My mother died the day before I was four years old. My stepmother died when I was eight and my father died when I was ten. My stepsister put me in an orphanage. She could have had me at home but she wanted the money. So I went for about two years. I think my father knew he was dying. I could talk to him. He would pick me up and put me on his knee.

My aunt said I had killed my mother. I told Dad and he said it was a load of rubbish. I remember it was a brilliant summer's day. He took me by the hand outside and there was a big white cloud. There was a bright light at the edges of the cloud. "Look up there! There she is smiling at you," he said. Aunty Florence left.

In many ways I was spoilt. I had everything done for me. When I got to the orphanage I couldn't even button up the back of my dress. I vowed that if I had children they would be independent of me.

I was fostered to a family at age thirteen. I stayed with them for twelve months. My foster mother found out she could get more money from the Polish workers who worked in the factory. I came home from school one day and she said "don't put your coat there, you're leaving". So I went to another family then. The people from the orphanage arranged for me to have lessons in shorthand and typing. The man there was horrible, he'd say "don't waste paper, you're not having to pay for it". I only stayed ten weeks. I said I wasn't going any more. I went to work in a cotton factory. I was there just over a year. They said if I wanted to do anything else I was to save up for it. I saved my money to go on a course. I had to pay board and travel but I did it. The course (adding and calculating) was a lot of money - £50.

In Oldham, the people there wanted to adopt me. I had to see a judge in chambers. He was wearing red robes. I said I wanted to be adopted because I didn't want to go back to the orphanage. I didn't have anyone to talk to.

I earned six pounds, twelve shillings and six pence which more than my adoptive father and this was the reason that they wanted to adopt me. My adoptive mother took it and gave me ten shillings out of that. Out of that I had to pay for my bus fare to Manchester and my lunch. So I used to have what they called a three-penny bap, but I did it. My adoptive father called me 'Lady Muck of Turd Hall' just because I wanted to have clean knickers every day. I'd always been used to having clean underwear. He told me to buy my own soap powder.

I used to leave the house at seven in the morning get to my office and do my work. I then found out that they had a ballet class in Old Trafford. So after work I didn't go home. I went to the ballet club. I'd get home by ten o'clock. I was very short of money and I had to have ballet shoes. So I got myself a Saturday afternoon job as a waitress, which paid for my shoes. When the local football team came the men would leave you a big tip.

Through dance I could give expression. They said I was a good mime artist. They didn't realise that I was getting rid of unhappiness.

At eighteen I decided I didn't want to live with them any more. I went nursing. I shared with a girl I went to school with. It gave me a place with a roof over my head. I met my husband, Alan, there in Bolton. We've been married fifty-three years.

You had to be hard to survive it. I always remember when I was a little girl of eight years old, there was a rough family near us who were always swearing. "Don't play with them" dad said. They paid for their daughter to go to a private school.

One morning I was crying, she called my dad a silly bugger.

Every week I'd go swimming at school but my father didn't know about it. I forgot and came home and said "I hate Joyce Nuttall". "Now what is it you see in Joyce you do not like in yourself?" my dad replied. He didn't reprimand me after that.

My father used to mess about with herbs and make concoctions. It was too expensive in those days to get the doctor. My dad would make medicines. People would come from miles around to get my dad's concoctions.

One day I found a baby fox and I put it in my basket. I called this fox Rudy because she was red. I couldn't put her in the barn with the other animals in case he transmitted infections. She was like a dog. We had her for a good few years. Then the farmer came and said Rudy had killed his sheep. So we had to get rid of Rudy or Dad would have gone to prison. Another two weeks on and the farmer's own dog killed a sheep. I was so annoyed. I put on my best clogs and went to the town hall. I went to the mayor's office. He invited me to come round where he was sitting. "Now, young lady, what do you want?" he said. "You had my Rudy killed and it wasn't her" I said and kicked his shins. "Take this little hellion out!" the mayor started shouting. Then I was taken home. My father said "I apologise for her behaviour" and he said he'd sort me out. I didn't get shouted at. I was told I shouldn't have done it, but then Rudy shouldn't have been killed either. My dad told me that what I had to learn in life was that two wrongs don't make a right. My dad bought me some gerbils but I never liked them.

So there was a lot in my early life that prepared me.

Up to three weeks ago I was having very bad nights. I'd get up and make a cup of tea. I needed to talk to someone. I trained as a psychodynamic counsellor and I thought, do what you told your patients. I wrote down my thoughts. I want my children to read them before anyone else. There's a lot of sadness there.

People are frightened of dying but I welcome death as a friend.

When I first knew I wrote a letter to my children for them to read and to tell them not to grieve, and to be happy because I am where I want to be.

I'm not brave. I'm being me. It's what's called 'inner spirit'. I've been doing negotiations with the Macmillan nurse because they aren't allowed to come into your home any more. I discussed mercy killing. They said they understood. The doctor said it was selfish. A meeting was arranged but I could not get to Sandwell. So a meeting has been arranged for my family to meet with the specialist palliative care nurse on the 20th July. My son lives in Quinton but is never in the country. I call him 'the hatchet man'. My daughter lives in Surrey.

*Doreen died at home a few weeks after she had told her story to us. She was cared for by her husband and daughter at home with support from many other people and support services. At her funeral her son gave a very fitting tribute to his mother and her funeral was carried out to her instructions and Gracie Fields was indeed played.

Two Peas in a Pod

Lenford's story told by Babs

"Like the sunshine breaking through on a bright summer's day
the lovely fragrance fills the air"

1998. Len told me twice he'd been to the toilet and seen a streak of blood. I told him we should keep an eye on it. So we went to the GP and he said that to be on the safe side it should be checked out. I asked for Len to see the consultant at the hospital. I knew him because by profession I am a theatre nurse.

The following week they checked him out with the camera and the week after that they did a biopsy. "I'm sorry, it's colon cancer" the doctor said. Len went in on the Tuesday and had the operation on Thursday. He was still in the recovery room. "Come and have a coffee" one nurse said. Another nurse gave me the thumbs up. She had scrubbed up for the op.

The consultant said to me "he's a lucky man. I think we caught it just in time". A friend came with me for the result. "There's no point giving treatment because there's nothing to treat" the doctor said.

It was 9th July 1998. They said they would check Lenford every three months.

In the January we went on a cruise. You see after the operation Len decided to retire so that we could spend more time together. We were like two peas in a pod. Lots of people said that. We decided to go places together. He was doing so well.

In June 2004 Len had a pain in his shoulder. At first he put it down to mowing the lawn. After two weeks of spraying it and rubbing it we went to the NEC to see an exhibition. We had to stop the car because the pain in Len's shoulder was so bad. "It could be a trapped nerve" the doctor said.

A fortnight later the doctor saw him and said that to be on the safe side he would send him for an X ray. They said they'd phone us in seven days, but that same day they phoned us. We picked up the message from the surgery...

For three years they had been doing check-ups. The colonoscopy in March had been clear.

Then the doctor said "I think the monster has raised its head again."

We went to the hospital and saw the doctor. It was June. "There's a shadow on the lungs and if it is cancer I don't know if it is an old one or a new one. To make sure, we need to do a biopsy" he said. That Monday he went in for the biopsy but the result was inconclusive.

Then they did a second one. We waited. It came back inconclusive.
We asked why it was coming back 'inconclusive'. "We are so sorry we have to put you through this again" they said.

Len was sent to a doctor at the chest clinic. "I want you in on Monday. We'll do a bronchoscopy – we'll go in through the nose" he said. We went back on the Friday and again we were told the result was 'inconclusive'.

We were told they needed to continue the investigations. We were sent to see a specialist at another hospital. They said that they would have to cut Len all the way around the back to get the biopsy. They told us that they would get him into hospital within two weeks. Within a week he was in hospital. They sent off his specimen there and then. It came back – 'inconclusive'.

More samples were sent through. Len saw the doctor on 25th July and was told that he did have cancer.

In November he started on chemo tablets. When he went back after three months he had a bone scan. He was put on a different chemo. The good news was that Len hadn't been sick and the cancer had started to shrink.

After another twelve weeks the hospital told us that they weren't happy. It wasn't working as well as they liked. We were told that they would put Len on an intravenous chemotherapy and tablets and that they would have side effects - numbness and black spots on the skin.

Every time Len went the cancer was not getting any bigger, but it wasn't shrinking either.

The numbness increased and it got worse when Len stood up. He couldn't feel his feet. It was difficult for him to shave because he couldn't feel his fingers. He would drop the razor.

Lenford went back and had another twelve sessions after that.

You see in our relationship before all this when I had been ill and Lenny worked he'd leave me a tray of water and a flask of soup before he left for work. He'd run the bath for me when he got home. He'd help me and he'd cook dinner. If I woke in the night in pain he would come to my side. That was the kind of person he was.

It was the 26th October 2006. "There's good news and bad news" the registrar said. "The cancer hasn't got any bigger, but it is also no smaller. The numbness is getting worse so I will have to take you off this treatment. For a few weeks we will keep a check on your blood and we will see you again on the 12th December".

Len's weight was going a bit but it wasn't too bad.

By 5th November that year it was a struggle for Len to come down the stairs. I remember jumping up to help him – his legs were going.

On the Sunday night, he started to vomit. Right through his illness he hadn't had that problem. Only once I had had to take him to the hospital with a high temperature. It was a urine infection and he was OK after three days.

I told the doctor and the emergency district nurse came. Then they came with special bed equipment.

Len was meant to go back on the 12th December but the doctor from the hospital rang and said he would see him before then at the hospital.

I asked for an ambulance for when they measured him up for radiotherapy. They measured him on the Thursday and gave him the radiotherapy treatment on the Friday.

The following Monday we went to see Len's doctor. We sat down. He said "Lenford, Lenford, me old buddy. I don't know how to put this. Now your mobility has gone, so all we can do is to make you as pain free as possible. What we'll do is see if we can get you in a hospice for a week".

Lenny was sad. The doctor assured him that the move to the hospice was not permanent. Len said "I want to go back home". "Look I've got a good team and we'll get things moving" the doctor said. Lenny said "I know Babs has been doing everything". That was the time that I just passed out, fainted.

The following day my daughter Jackie answered the phone to the doctor. "How's your mum?" he asked. I talked to him. "How are you feeling? You know it's probably exhaustion. It's probably as well to get things moving. Your first Macmillan nurse works here now" he said.

Lenny was really sad. "I want to come home" he said again.

The two occupational therapy people came and said that it wouldn't be ideal for him to go home until everything was set up for him.

The woman from hospice at home came and said that the mattress wasn't good enough. Things were shifted up to the loft and after a week new things came. "Thanks for getting me out of that place" Lenny said when he came home and he never stopped thanking me.

Back at home he was doing pretty well. They set up a syringe driver for over Christmas. He wasn't eating much, just sipping tea, energy drinks. Family from America came. He managed to open presents he wasn't too bad.

Days later he was crying out in pain. He was trying to pull himself up. I could see that the weight was dropping off his legs. I made sure of these things: that he had nice clean pyjamas on, that his body was creamed, and that he was shaved and after-shave put on.

At four o'clock on the Tuesday evening, even though he was dosed up that terrible pain came again. I had to ring the medical people up.

Wednesday he just about opened his eyes and that evening he called me to say the Lord's Prayer with him.

On Thursday morning his morphine drip was increased. The doctor said that at best Lenford had twenty-four to forty-eight hours to live.

I used a little syringe to squirt a bit of water into his mouth.

On the 6th January his breathing was shallow and his pulse was weak. I sat by his bed talking.

On the Saturday night Jackie and a neighbour let me have a break on the settee. I wasn't sleeping. At 7 am I went to the bathroom and to the kitchen for tablets. Jackie called me in and said his breathing was different. He was gasping for breath. I held his hands again and then the words came to me "Len, He's waiting for you. He's calling you home. You are very special and He's got work for you to do. Honey, can you see that light shining? Hold onto His hand. You won't fall. Don't worry about me. One day I will follow that light and be with you".

I said "Jackie, he's gone. Get the notepad and put the time".

We started to phone friends. The doctor came. He left a letter to take to the GP. The Funeral Director came to assess the body and he told us to turn off the central heating and to open the windows. I asked for a little more time because some friends were coming. He gave us a little time and then he phoned and said, "I'm sorry we have to take him now". I went upstairs and looked out of the bedroom window. It didn't seem real. When I came down I saw an empty bed and all the equipment. Is Lenny really gone? I thought.

He had been telling me how much he loved me and worried about me. When Jackie was little she had called Len 'Podgy One' and me 'Podgy Two'. A week before he died he said "my name is Lenford." He spelt it out. "You have to get it right for the funeral people" he said.

Lenny died on the 7th of January.

I knew Len wouldn't want anyone else to officiate at the funeral but our minister Glen was away, so we waited until he returned. I organised the funeral, which took place on the 2nd February.

He had a wonderful turn out. People I hadn't seen for twenty years came. I was getting phone calls from all over the world. Sometimes you feel like ripping the phone out, but you are also glad that they have wanted to call.

There were all these big boxes of flowers by the door. The place was like a shrine – arrangements and baskets. I'm glad some of the flowers arrived in vases because I wouldn't have had enough for them all. It was wonderful. I had £735 off people, which went to cancer charities. The whole place was covered with cards. I had phone calls from support groups, doctors and it did help.

My godson got married in Jamaica this year. They had the party when they came back. I was sad because Lenny wasn't there and it had been such a lovely day.

When I went to the opera on the 7th July I came home and wanted to tell Lenny what a wonderful girl the singer was, only twenty-three and such a magnificent voice. It's things like that. The house feels so empty. Even watching the tennis yesterday I wanted to share it with Lenny.

The good thing is I'm sleeping better. A month after his death I'd get up at about 1 am to make a drink. I'd just be sitting there crying.

Yesterday I said "Lenny, you'd be proud of me. I had lamb and three roast potatoes and broccoli for my dinner". I felt so full. At least, thank God, I've put a bit of weight back on. At church they tell me I'm looking well but my fears are still there.

Sometimes I go upstairs and I come down to lock up. There is such emptiness. Still in the morning I am in floods of tears and I say to myself "no, no, no, he's not coming back".

I am glad, blessed and thankful that I was there, holding my Lenny's hand.

An Angel on the Pillow

Harold's story told by Dot

"Always the life and soul wherever you went,
Chasing the dark clouds away"

Harold was back and forth from hospital. He was in hospital for fifteen weeks. His lungs were filling up. He had a tube in him and they took six litres of liquid from him. He was Chair of Age Well and he wanted to carry on.

He wanted a chair lift because he didn't want to be stuck down in the living room. He wanted his own bed. Our daughter contacted SAFA and they told us they got bits of funding from ATS, Burma Star to get the stair lift.

He was a big man. He wasn't always like that. Both of us did voluntary work for thirty years for the elderly and disabled.

Harold went into the license trade.

He worked for British Steel. We both took early retirement, but he couldn't. We worked voluntarily for the council. Harold would drive; I was escort. He was one of those men who liked entertaining. "You go home and tell your mother what you've been doing with Harold" he'd say to the kids on the bus.

I did the medicines and that.

Harold had all the fishing gear. All the kids in Sandwell – he'd teach them fishing. We've got a big garden and he'd show them how to cast out and all that. Since then some of the kids have taken it up. This little fishing rod, one of my daughters bought him to take on his holiday. He'd go to Knightwick in Worcester way. He'd go fishing in all weathers. Sometimes he'd have to chip the ice away. "You'll catch pneumonia" his mother would say.

We got children from Blakely School and put them together with the elderly. They loved it. The children got to appreciate the elderly. When we retired they gave us a cut glass vase and they made us a book. We loved the kids, wherever they were from and whatever they were like. After a few weeks they phoned us up and asked us back.

When Harold died his mind was OK. People would still ring him up for help. He would go on his scooter and the ring and ride. He never stopped going to meetings.

He gradually lost weight.

We had a last holiday in June in Eastbourne at a disabled hotel. On that holiday in Eastbourne he got this toy, a fluffy dog, and I've still got it.

One of the carers came down. Harold had been coughing and bleeding. He had to go into hospital. He was full of cancer. He'd tap his side. He would joke about getting fat on one side of his stomach, but it was cancer.

He had an electric bed put downstairs. The hospice nurses would come. His eyes went so they would have to put drops in. "What nationality are you?" he would say to carers who came to our house, and if they were Indian he would jabber away in that language.

My daughter works at the hospital where Harold was a patient so she was there when they told him. I was at home. She said she'd be there because "our Dad never tells you what's going on when he sees the doctor". This time the doctor said "Harold we keep bringing you in and chatting. There's nothing more we can do, but you have an open invitation if there is anything wrong. You know what's coming Harold. You've got cancer" the doctor said. "Right, I can have a drink then now can I?" Harold replied.

"Mam, Dad's coming home he's got cancer" my daughter said when she came home. I was lucky I got my daughters who are all in the medical field. Of course they could organise things.

He was badly dehydrated. They said he'd have to go in for an overnight stay. He went in the next day with our daughter Gillian. When they said they'd keep him in my daughter said "no he's going home. We know what to do". The doctor came and said "I've never heard anything like it. It's all arranged for this man".

You see we knew we'd got six rugby boys, grandsons, and we only had to phone them for their help. So they got him home. We drew up and the lads were waiting. We opened the French window. Even though there's a slope on the drive they managed it. We got him off the trolley. We put him in his bed.

The specialist palliative care nurse asked me how I felt. I said "I don't know what to expect". It did help, talking. I had carers and I did some of the work. For weeks I did it by myself and it got too much. Carers came during the day and nurses came in the evening. "We're sending her out now" they'd say to him. I'd go sometimes to the Catholic Church Bingo Club. "She can use her own money" Harold would say. I'd leave stuff out for the night nurses: a pillow, a quilt. "It's lovely coming here. It's a home from home" they'd say.

The last days were terrible. It was November. He hadn't been very good. The nurse came.

All of a sudden he took his rings off and he said, "we've had a good innings." But he kept hanging on. He kept going. We reached our sixty years anniversary, which he wanted. We couldn't go on a cruise because they wouldn't insure him. We booked a holiday for Christmas it cost £1000. I had a hard job to give that holiday away. I did eventually to someone who wasn't very well. So it did somebody some good. "You're not doing as you're told. You've got to give that holiday away" Harold kept saying. He was like that.

In the last week of his life I remember he shouted "turn that off". There wasn't anything on.

My daughter Gillian said "I know Dad you're waiting for your favourite daughter's birthday" which was on the 14th December. He did too. He died on the 15th.

Our daughter Marilyn was out shopping and she'd got stuck in traffic. We phoned her and told her to come. She just got to the front door when it happened. She took it very bad for a while.

Marilyn my daughter said "Mum you're doing very well. Dad would have wanted you to go on holiday". We went to Tenerife. We just relaxed. It did us good. I'm still – sometimes I cry. A couple of weeks ago I wasn't very well and I cried. I talk to him.

My son in law is jolly. He takes me to the bingo on a Monday. He talks to Harold he says "she's spending all your money".

When I went to bed on the day I buried him, I could have sworn he was in that room. I heard "Dottie, Dottie, Dottie".

I often hear his voice. In the morning I'll hear "are you alright?"

My daughters say the same. His voice is plain. The words are plain.

In bed I'll read a bit.

I say "Good night. God Bless". Even when I go to the crem, I've got him in one of those sanctums, I say "I'm here".

When I went into the doctor's last week, I said "I'm fine". "You're allowed to be weepy" she said.

I'm not well myself. I've got leukaemia and I've got a son with leukaemia. A Myeloproliferative disorder. It has stabilised. I take chemo tablets and some for depression. Some days I sit and feel like I want to sit and do nothing, but there's no good stopping in the house. I try to help other people. They call me the carer. They keep telling me to look after myself.

They are doing a memorial for Harold.

"We bought in teas and a juicer and also aloe vera." - Baksho

"He was the man." - Barbara

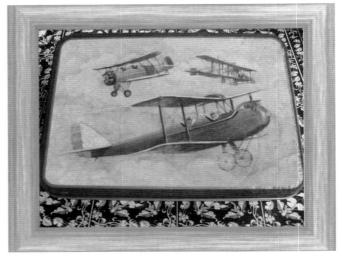

"Your love of flying your planes..." - Sheila

Dot's locket: a photo of Harold

Bob's Birmingham & District Works Amateur Football Association medal

Lenford's cufflinks.

"Be strong, think positive." - Kay

"Through dance I could give expression."
- Doreen

"Life is like an eternal flame." - Gill

"I went on holiday. I wore a bikini." - Angela

33

I've still got this stair lift. Sometimes I stumble so I'm not getting rid of it. They're going to remove the outdoor lift because I think it's a reminder and it makes you vulnerable.

When Harold had his eightieth birthday the kids put balloons on the lift outside. We had a garden party. It was lovely.

He arranged all his own funeral. When he was cremated he wore everything he'd worn for the sixtieth. He had played 'My Way.' Harold chose that because he used to sing. He'd go to entertain in hospitals. He'd sing along to the telly. We'd go to holiday places and he'd go into the competitions – he always won.

At the funeral they played 'The Last Post' and 'Danny Boy' his dad's favourite. He had the Burma Star. The place was full. He had this disc made. I can still play it. My eldest daughter Debbie, she wrote 'Our Dad.' It was a tribute to Harold. She'd written about how he was the eldest in the family and how his brothers and sisters went into cottage homes. She got in all his life from what he did in the army right through to the end. The Vicar read it because my daughter couldn't. Lots of people said his funeral was marvellous.

They said he was a big man because he was a big man in every way. He also read a lot.

When I got back from the crem there was a bouquet of flowers and this ring and a card. Harold had made sure that was there for me. The night he died my daughter took me down to her house to sleep there and she'd put a guardian angel on the pillow.

My thoughts go back to this time last year, I will never forget. Such a sad time, seeing my dear Harold struggling to stay with us. It was hard and we were helpless, we could not do anything. It broke our hearts to see him suffer like that, but we would not want him in pain, which he must have been. He never let us know how he felt. He used to say "I'm alright, don't worry". It was an awful time, but a blessing when he finally went to sleep. We all miss him so much, but I'm sure he is still around us, keeping his beady eye on us all. Little things happen, and I hear sounds. Sometimes I'm sure I hear him speak. His presence is felt very much around the house. I'll talk to him as if he was here, tell him all what goes on each day, it makes me feel good.

Treasure

Bill's story told by Gill

"A fresh bounce in your step as you made the tea, everything done so precisely.
The spring in your step was the song in my heart."

Every ending has to have a beginning, so that is where I will start – the beginning of my husband's end of life. My husband William (whom we will call Bill, which he preferred) had not been a well man for a number of years. In 1984 Bill was very ill with heart problems and underwent open heart surgery for a valve replacement after which his life changed. There were a number of things he was no longer able to do. Gardening was one of his passions, even though I had to point out which were weeds and which were plants.

Bill had spent many years working in hospitals as a theatre porter and had seen many patients to and from their operations. He was a compassionate man, especially with children. When he took a child to theatre he would put on a funny hat to comfort them. He was a people's friend. He carried on working as long as he could, but it was in a different capacity. Because of his heart problems, which effectively caused his body to slow down, his work involvement became very limited. Hospital visits became more frequent due to unstable angina.

By this time he was working for Social Services. Bill would be on the door, directing the public to various departments and sorting the mail out. He loved his job - again it was about meeting and helping others. As time went on his hours at work became less. Even though it was part-time his unstable angina and not being fully functional to carry out his duties meant he was eventually certified medically unfit. He found it hard not to be working and helping with the family income.

We had two children, a son, Philip, who lives in Yorkshire and a daughter, Stephanie. Going back to the time just before his heart surgery, it was the year our daughter was married, 1984. Bill, although not well at that time, was determined to walk our daughter down the aisle. He was very unsteady on his feet, but, oh boy, was he a proud man.

As time passed, which brings me to the beginning of the next chapter in his life, Bill began to have a lot of back pain. He also had pains in his legs. The pains in his legs were not unusual because of his poor circulation, and did not cause too much concern. Then he had problems with his plumbing as I called it, but because he was on so much medication, which caused

him to use the bathroom more frequently, it sort of masked another underlying problem.
I became concerned when his visits to the bathroom became not only frequent, but his
length of time spent there became longer. So on our next visit to the GP I mentioned it. The
doctor then gave us a few words of information about what was needed to be done. Within
two weeks Bill received an appointment from the hospital to see a consultant, who on the
visit confirmed abnormalities of the prostate, which would require further investigations.

Our next visit to the consultant was for the results after having a body scan. We set off with
mixed feelings, not really knowing what to expect. On arriving at the side room on the second floor we found it full of patients waiting to be seen by consultants. We found seats and
waited for Bill's name to be called. I looked around and wondered if they were all there for
the same reason.

I looked for the consultancy nursing specialist hoping she would be there, as we had met her
on our first visit. I found her to be a very warm and reassuring person. There was a TV in
the room – I glanced at it occasionally but my thoughts were elsewhere.

Eventually, Bill's name was called by the consultancy nursing specialist. "Come on William,
how have you been?" she said. She had a warm smile as she looked across at Bill. She is the
kind of person that has a way about her that gives you a feel good factor about yourself. It
lifts your spirits up whatever your thoughts or feelings are at the time. We took our places,
each looking at each other (that is Bill and myself). Then the crunch came. The consultant
explained the situation and confirmed that it was prostate cancer, but there were also sec-
ondaries. It had gone into his bones. I can't really explain my feeling and thoughts at that
point. Bill turned and looked at me. We clasped each other's hand.

When we were told the consultant said the good news was that it was treatable and that Bill
would receive injections in the lower stomach area near the groin. I was listening, but at the
same time my thoughts seemed to be far off as though it was a dream I suppose. But no,
this was reality.

The injections (Zoladex) would be administered by the nurse and would be for about two
years or until his body needed different or stronger medication. Our first visit for the injection was one of apprehension – would it work? Our lovely nurse was again very reassuring.
The injection was given on the right side, with a small dressing applied. It was then that I
asked her the main question. Now my mind was clearer, as was Bill's. "The consultant said
it was treatable, but is it curable?" I said to her. The Nurse knew what I was going to ask.
Her reply was no, but she said there were treatments such as injections that could help to
slow the progression rate down.

Again she had that way of putting your mind at ease. Our next visit to her was quite funny
really. Before going to the hospital Bill shaved the space for the injection. He just smiled at
her and said "I have come prepared". "Well I'm sorry William, but it's the left side this time,
we alternate the injections" she replied. We just laughed about it. I was glad Bill had seen
the funny side of it, although he had a very dry sense of humour. On the way home from

our visit with the results, we just had a time of silence, each with our own thoughts. "Well that's that then" Bill said, but what he meant was "well now we know".

The next part of Bill's life, plus my own, was to accept the situation. We both attended church and had a lot of faith. I knew that whatever we thought, said or did would not alter the situation or circumstances. We had to come to a point of acceptance to enable us to move forward to be able to cope with the weeks and months ahead of us. Bill was very strong, he had an inner strength that kept him going. He didn't let anything faze him. We accepted each day as it came and I treated each day as normal.

Eventually, time took its toll on Bill's body. Pain was becoming a real factor. He could not have certain medication because of his heart problems.

Our next appointments to see the consultant were via a wheelchair, which Bill at one stage was reluctant to use. Our nurse, as usual, was there and I saw the compassion that she had when she saw the pain Bill was in. It was then arranged for him to stay in hospital for palliative care. He became upset because he had told me from the start that he did not want to lie in a hospital bed or hospice. He had been in and out of hospital for a number of years with other problems. I promised that I would take care of him at home, after all I had worked for social services for a number of years in the caring profession, plus I had nursing experience. Having said that, it is a different ball game when it is your loved one. Once again, the nurse reassured him and told him that he would only be there for his course of treatment to be sorted out so that life would be more comfortable for him.

Yes, he did come back home. The nurse had contacted Bridges, a support group, also Hospice at Home. These support groups proved to be invaluable. By this time Bill was confined to his chair. I had already reverted to single beds so that it was easier for me to attend to him. Of course in due time it was easier for two to assist, one either side of the bed.

Bill was a typical family man and loved his grandchildren. It was nearing the end of September and his thoughts were on Christmas so that we could still do our Christmas shopping together, I got the Argos catalogue and Woolworth's and any books that Bill requested to see and look through. By the end of October we had our gifts all bought and wrapped up. We had achieved it together.

It really touched me that on Christmas day, nearly three weeks after he died there was a gift for me. There was even a Christmas card saying that he was thinking about me.

Bill was deteriorating slowly and noticeably. His eating habits became different. In a long part of his last few years he had always been careful of his food intake, i.e. low fat et cetera, because of his heart condition. I asked him one day what he would like for tea. "Proper chips" was his reply. He meant home made. I had not cooked those for a long time. I hadn't got a fryer, because it had been so long. So I purchased one that day and we had 'proper chips' for tea. I must admit, not only was it good to see Bill eating, but also I enjoyed them myself. Whatever Bill requested I endeavoured to supply. Although he was not eating a lot, at least he enjoyed what he had. At the end of the day, did it really matter what he ate? A healthy diet was not the issue at that time.

He was a very determined man. He did not want to use the commode. Once when he did I couldn't get him off it. He was really trying to get up but it was sapping his energy. It was in the night. "Let me call for one of the carers" I said. It was painful for him because he had bedsores and because he was on warfarin. If he bled he would really bleed.

I mentioned earlier that the nurse had put us on to Bridges, a support group. We had literature come through the post as she had already registered us with them. The next step was a visit from them. I think at that time I had a few mixed feelings. Although we had come to terms with the situation, this was to be a sort of confirmation that Bill's life had reached another stage. Bridges told us of the support they offer. The staff were very caring and provided genuine support for us. There were a couple of times when we had to travel from the hospital. Bridges supplied the taxi fare, or if they had transport available then we had a driver supplied by them. Bridges helped to take any worries or concerns off us regarding financial help to and from the hospital.

There came a time when Bill was in hospital again for a blood transfusion. Again our nurse reassured him that he would not be in long. It was on this occasion that our daughter met the nurse and had time for a chat about her dad. The nurse is a very busy person, but she always found time to answer questions or give professional advice. Stephanie our daughter had high praise for her. She, or should I say we as a family, knew that Bill was receiving the best possible care.

As time went on the treatment for Bill was not working. Another scan proved to us that his bones were becoming weaker. This was when Hospice at Home started to call. They would monitor his pain and adjust morphine when necessary. Hospice at Home became part of the family. We met most of the team, but one of the specialist palliative care nurses was who we saw more of. The first time they came, as soon as the front door was opened, it was as though we had known them for a while, like 'one of the family'.

On a Thursday the Hospice at Home care assistant would come and sit with Bill while I had some time out. I have a friend, Kath, and when we would be ready to go out Bill always gave me some money and would say "that's for you and Kath to have something to eat and drink". Each time we shopped Bill would always ask me to bring chocolate raisins, scotch egg and a box of Dairy Lea cheese spreads. As soon as we returned he would request a cheese triangle and enjoy devouring it.

There were times when Kath would visit and we would be doing a jigsaw puzzle. Bill would be asleep in his chair, or so we thought, because sometimes we would be talking and all of a sudden Bill would reply to something we had said with an amusing little quip. On one occasion we were doing a puzzle and had got a box of chocolates open. Kath suddenly said "oh I've managed to fit a piece of the puzzle in". "Have another chocolate" Bill replied his eyes still shut. We looked across at him. He had a broad grin on his face. We just laughed.

Bill developed pressure sores so district nurses were coming in three times a week. The district nurses were also very approachable and friendly. Our home was becoming a hive of activity. Although I managed to take care of Bill myself, washing, getting him out of bed, it became apparent that it needed two people to handle him. By this time we had obtained a hospital bed. It was a great help when it came to getting Bill in and out of bed. Also it was more comfortable for him.

I tried to give Bill as much independence as possible. When it came to drinks I purchased a non-spill mug from the chemist so that he could have a drink and not have me standing over him in case he spilt it or dozed off to sleep with it still in his hand, which was often the case. He would always be sorry if he caused extra washing with accidents, or got me up in the night for whatever the reason. But I would just reassure him and say it was OK. If it had been the other way round he would have done the same for me. We were there for each other, no matter what.

Bill would often talk about his grandchildren. Nerissa, Stephanie's eldest daughter, who was fourteen at the time, would text me every morning enquiring about her granddad before going to school. Her text would read "Hi Nan, how's Grandad? - Truth". So I would text back with the truth. I think it is important that we are open and honest to the truth when children ask for it. Nerissa was only just fourteen but her lasting memories of her granddad are that she knew the truth about why he is no longer with us. She had a good tutor at school who was her mentor. Obviously, she misses her grandad, but she knows that he is out of any pain and suffering.

During the day of Wednesday 6th December, Bill became very quiet and did not want to be disturbed. A carers group had been coming in to help me with his personal care. Bill, on that morning, was very weak and did not want the bother of being messed about with. I gently washed his hands and face myself. He stayed in bed and was asleep more than awake. I spent most of the day in the bedroom with him. The district nurse came and saw the situation and left him to rest, but told me that if I needed her to give her a call.

During the night that followed Bill's breathing had changed. I had been awake as usual in case he needed me. I knew within my heart that it was the turning point. When daylight appeared I got dressed and made myself a drink, then sat in the bedroom talking to Bill and stroking his hand. He squeezed my hand and gently said that I was a 'treasure'. I told him that he was too. We are all treasures.

During the last few days prior to 6th December we decided as a family not to have any more visitors, that is outside visitors. We have lots of friends at church and on occasions they would visit, but we decided that we needed quality time together as a family. When Bill was first diagnosed we had a week away with my daughter, son-in-law and the two girls, Nerissa and Bryony. It will be a holiday the girls will always remember.

7th December. It was now 9 am. I telephoned my daughter to inform her of her dad's deterioration. The district nurse was not due to call that day, but I knew that Hospice at Home would be with me shortly. When she arrived it was not the specialist palliative care nurse, as I think she was on holiday, but nevertheless even though I hadn't met this lady before it was just like I had. She did inform me that Bill was quite poorly and it didn't matter if I left his medication, which at this point he would not have been able to swallow. Our GP was asked to call in.

The Pastor of our church rang to enquire on how Bill was doing. When I explained he came straight away and waited with me until Steph arrived with Haydn, my son-in-law. They stayed for a while then had to go, but would return later. The GP came and explained that there was nothing more really that could be done. He was very caring and waited for a short while with me, as my son Phillip was on his way from Yorkshire. We just sat talking about life itself and Bill's situation. The GP had to go as he too was a busy man. He did say that it was good that he came. I think he was interested in Bill's life history.

My son arrived with Joshua, his youngest son. By now it was mid-afternoon. I just sat by Bill's bed talking to him. Kath arrived and she came and we sat on my bed reflecting on the past few weeks. We both knew that it would not be long before Bill would slip away. Joshua came into the room. He was ten years old. Kath looked at me and said "do you think he should be in here?" I thought for a moment, after all it was his grandad he had come to see. I didn't reply. It was just then that Bill slipped away, out of his suffering and pain. I thank God that he did not suffer too much unbearable pain, which does happen with bone cancer.

Our son Phil and daughter Steph came in, but Josh who was present just got up, went to his granddad, took hold of his hand, kissed him and said "goodbye, Grandad". That night my son and family stayed. Bill had been taken. His hospital bed lay empty. I got into bed, looked across to where he had been lying and I whispered good night and God bless. Suddenly a little person came and crept into bed with me – it was Josh. His mom and dad looked into the bedroom and asked if he was okay being there. I looked at Josh and asked if he wet the bed. "No" he quickly replied. "That's OK then, you can stay" I said. Then I nudged him after a minute or two and said "I forgot to tell you, I do."

Next thing was the funeral arrangements. Kath, my friend, was with me. Steph was not able to be there through seeing to family. The funeral went well, although it's like going through the motions. It's like wondering if it's a dream. At a later date we had a celebration service of Bill's life. Although tributes were paid at the funeral, this was a chance for everyone else that wanted to pay tribute to do so. We had been in the church for a number of years, working with the young people as well as the elderly. I was surprised at how much impact we had made on other people. The youth paid their respects through song and dance and Nerissa was one of them. She had also done a poem. We also gave a cheque to Hospice at Home and the specialist palliative care nurse had come to receive it. I had also invited Bill's key nurse and to my delight she was able to attend. Hospice at Home gave a few words on their role in the community. Bill's nurse, after being put on the spot, explained who she was. In all it was a very good day. We had refreshments and the church was full of well wishers for myself and the family.

In all this I think coping with it after accepting the situation has made me a stronger person. When I first learnt about it I knew that I had to be strong for my children. My reactions would reflect on them and consequently they had to be strong for my grandchildren (their children). The grandchildren attended the funeral. I think it's important that children see life as it really is; they know the closing chapter to Grandad's life. Perhaps later in their lives they won't be asking questions about it, but giving answers to others in the same situation. Throughout all this I know that our faith in God gave both Bill and I an inner strength that saw us through and enabled us to see beyond our capabilities and situation.

This is not the end of the story. It is just goodbye for a little while. One day we shall meet again in the presence of our Lord and Saviour and that is the hope, which keeps us, going. Accepting the situation does not mean you have given up. It means that you are dealing with it and it does make you stronger for what is to come.

The following days and weeks I was kept busy sorting things out. It is a strange feeling when your home, which was once a very busy hive of activity, changes. All of a sudden you have lost your loved one and the professional friends that you had coming in each day. I say friends because that's what they became, as I said before, part of the family. Now you are on your own but then life goes on. Hospice at Home came to see me to see how I was coping.

I was pleased when they invited me to an afternoon tea with them and with others in the same situation, but it also gave me a chance to meet again with the team that had been very much part of our life while Bill was so poorly. Their presence at such a sensitive time was invaluable and much appreciated. They were a listening ear outside of family and professional help and advice on various issues – medication of morphine. They helped make life more comfortable for Bill to be at home.

I've lived with multiple losses.

My mother died in 1945. Me and my twin brother were born in 1941. I think she was only about twenty-five years old when she died of TB and pleurisy. Then there was no cure.

We were sent to a children's home in Erdington. At the time my father was a prisoner of war. We were only seven when my father came home. To get your children back in those days the man had to either get a nanny or remarry. He remarried. She was the archetypal wicked stepmother. This scar on my chin is from her kicking me in the face. She would lock me in the coal house. Once when I was in there I heard a voice calling my name Gillian. I felt at peace. I thought it was my mother's voice. When my stepmother realised that I wasn't scared by the coal cellar any more she stopped putting me in there. She didn't do the same things to my sister because she was deaf and dumb. It was the window cleaner who reported the cruelty. My dad knew about it but there were issues with him too. He went to prison.

So I went back to the children's home. Erdington Cottage Homes. You were stigmatised if you were in a children's home. Initially me and my brother went together, but he was in home seven and I was in home twelve. I was in Windy Ridge.

An ambulance came up the drive and took my brother. They told me he would come back but he never did. I met him years later but not then. I kept running up the path wanting and waiting for him to come back. My sister was in another home.

I have a photo of us with her.

Also sadly a few years ago my son's child had a cot death. I got an early morning phone call. There was just this silence then "it's me". "What's wrong?" I said. "We've lost her" my son replied. He said his daughter's name. The last time we'd seen her was at her christening. She was nearly nine months when she died. My daughter was expecting at the same time. I thought I'd have to tell Bill the truth. "She's died" I said. Neither of us fell back asleep again. I couldn't wait for morning to come. The following morning I tried to phone my daughter to tell her but she wasn't there so I phoned my son in law. He works at a bank. "He's at the hospital at the moment" the receptionist there said. My daughter had gone into hospital. She'd had a miscarriage. I wished I could have dropped everything and gone.

My son carried that little coffin all the way to the grave. It was as though the whole village turned out. It was snowing.

Now to help me cope I keep busy. I am an active member in the church and help with the children's club, and both Bill and myself helped with this for a number of years. I tend to set myself targets, visiting places and people. I also write inspirational verse.

My grandchildren are never far away, especially Nerissa the older one – fifteen years old. She still texts me every day. I think I now text more than using the phone by voice, although I do text my sister who is deaf and dumb. I keep myself busy, but there is never a day when Bill is not in my thoughts. There is always something that jolts your memory. Little things that make you smile and remember the good times.

Life is like an eternal flame or candle within, it never really goes out. Not only do we recall memories, but our children have their thoughts and memories, as do our grandchildren. Memories of good times or perhaps not so good. Through words spoken. Times of laughter. Memories that are passed down, to live on in the heart of others.

A Black Country Lad

Bob's story

"Having a sense of humour has helped.
If you can laugh at these things you can get on."

I want to do this because if I can help someone else I will.

I was born in 1932, working class, I was in the forces and I met Sylvia my wife. We lived in Handsworth then we came here.

I used to be a governor at a large secondary school on the disciplinary committee, I was there for fourteen years and I loved it. I used to take Sylvia to work at the council and then used to go round to the school. I used to go away with them to outward bounds in South Wales. I used to be in the RAF. I was three years in paid service and five years in reserves. I did my training in England and then I was based in Germany for two and a half years. In those days it was called BAFO. That was 1951. They taught me to ski. Can you imagine me, a lad from the Black Country, skiing and playing tennis? Ooh it was great. I was stationed at Stafford when I came home.

After my diagnosis (for prostate cancer) I don't remember coming out of the hospital. My wife wasn't with me. My sister was with me.

I had been talking to my daughter on the phone and I had a terrible pain. I showed my doctor straight away and he collected some blood. During the tests they found a tumour on my kidney.

"The news is this" the consultant said "you've got a tumour on your right kidney, now I know you refused an operation on your neck but you can't refuse this. It's enormous, 27 centimetres. Also your tests for prostate cancer proved positive".

I remember it was the day before my son's birthday that I had the surgery. I was in high dependency for two days. The tumour was as big as your head. I'd had no symptoms and my bowels were fine.

"How long have I had this growing?" I asked. "You've had it growing for about four years and your prostate cancer for about ten years" the consultant said. The consultant went on to say that my lungs, liver and bones were fine.

When they opened me up for my kidney the tumour was the size of a football. They thought it was attached to the bowels, but they clamped them off. They were clear.

There are positives: I'm on tablets and now my blood pressure has dropped. Now I just take something for my cholesterol levels (which most older people have to) and an aspirin, that's all.

They looked after me at the hospital. I was eating two meals a day. They were fantastic.

My concern all along has been Sylvia, my wife. I'm her carer. I'd leave notes on the door saying 'have you got your keys?' She's got heart problems, and asthma very bad. So she's in and out of hospital.

We are silly as people, we depend on a car. When you've got a problem with the car you realise how much you depend on it. This area is hilly and getting the bus is difficult.

Two of our children live abroad. Without Bridges we'd have been in trouble. They've been fantastic.

When I went into hospital we'd got another little grandson on the way. I worried I wouldn't be around to see him.

To me it's been an experience, but if you're going to have it, enjoy it. Surgery started on April 17th 2007.

Before I went into this particular hospital the stories I had heard about it in the press and from other people, weren't great. I remember the nurse at my pre-med asking if I had any concerns. "Yes, MRSA" I said. They took swabs and they came out OK. The nurse asked me if I was using the disinfecting hand stuff and I said that I was and that I was even using it on my groin. "Don't do that you'll burn yourself!" she said. "Yes but it will get rid of the MRSA!" I replied laughing.

I feel I've been remarkably lucky. I enjoy everything. I was in the RAF. I enjoyed it. People say I'm a fighter.

When on my own doubts would come into my mind. At the cancer group talking helped. It was a kind of therapy. At the Cancer Support Group there are men at all different stages.

Even the consultants owned up and said they hadn't had cancer so they didn't know what I would be going through. When you know what you're fighting you know what you're fighting. You have to be positive. Sometimes I'd be positive to protect Sylvia. This is where support from Bridges and the Cancer Support Group is really invaluable. There are people there who've had different types of cancer and I've got an information booklet so I can understand what's going on. The information really helps.

After the operation the nurse said "you can go out tomorrow". She was taking the catheter out. She had to scan it. They scan your bladder. She said I'd got retention. She said I'd have to go out with a bag on my leg.

My three kids have done well. I wanted to be around for them. My dad died of lung cancer so it's one of the things I'm terrified of, but my dad was a smoker. He went down to six or seven stone. I thought I couldn't face that.

I've warned my two lads. My sons can say "my dad had prostate cancer". My dad also had water works trouble. He had a catheter fitted. It was crude in those days. He said he'd never have it done again, but they had to do it again. To the best of my knowledge he had prostate problems. My father was 65 when he died of lung cancer. When I had to go to hospital for radiotherapy alarm bells began to ring. I explained my fears of it, because they tattoo you, you know. In fact I followed everything they told me to: diet and drinking plenty of water. My side effects have been negligible. I was able to go on holiday a few days after treatment.

Before my surgery I was on Valium, I was in a bad way after receiving the news. I came off them. They told me to do it gradually but I just chucked them down the toilet. If I make my mind up that's it. Emotionally that was a difficult time. When I was on my own I didn't want to be in the dark. I was going into Sylvia at night to be comforted just like a child. If it came on telly - anything about suffering from cancer - I'd feel sorry for myself, but then if it was about kids I'd feel guilty then. But at the time I didn't know what the outcome would be.

Two days before I went into hospital I decorated the bedroom. I left my pin numbers for my wife and even chose hymns. Just in case. Me and Sylvia talked it out. Sylvia reassured me. We couldn't sleep well, that's why I was on Valium. We needed each other. It was traumatic for both of us. Sylvia had had a heart scare and with the kids being so far away... they were brilliant they'd ring every night.

I also remember that one of my testicles was as big as a pear. I didn't tell anyone not even Sylvia. I was worried it might be cancer. At the Cancer Support Group I talked to a man who described a similar thing and he told me it was infection. It was the same as me. I was relieved. It wasn't a consultant it was someone who had gone through it. At the time I was on a drug, which is a chemical castration.

Having a sense of humour has helped. If you can laugh at these things you can get on.

There is a neighbour who's had something similar to me but he is very ill. If I see his wife I don't always tell the whole truth about how well I'm feeling. I don't like saying I'm fine.

I had an operation on my throat thirty years ago. A couple of years ago they wanted to do another surgery. The consultant thought I was thirty-seven and I was seventy-three. That didn't fill me with confidence. Now they are undecided as to what to do with this one.

Years ago I'd got multiple nodules on my thyroid. I found the lump when I was shaving two years ago. The left lobe was removed thirty years ago. My sister and father had the same thing and it was a man named Campbell Cook who removed them for us all.

I went in two years ago as an outpatient. It was a camera they put up your nose. The consultant told me to lie on the couch. He put a swab on my shoulder. "We are now going to do a biopsy" he said. He put the needle into my neck, into my thyroid. It was painful.

"What we're contemplating is giving you medication for this at the hospital as they've got a nuclear department but we haven't decided yet" the consultant that I am seeing now says. That's why they want this scan. They say they may not do anything. I'm waiting for this appointment in February.

Now religion is a touchy subject. We are Methodists. To me we should respect each other's religions – it's just an interpretation of the same God. Having this illness has made me respect that more. At the time we did pray. We still do. Prayer is a very big factor in it. Before I went into surgery I was on the trolley and I thought, this is the last little trip, boy, for you on wheels. I wasn't scared because I'd made my peace. When I woke up in intensive care I thought, is this Hell? If it is I hope they've got some water because I'm parched.

When I went into hospital I had my own room and toilet. I was worried that that might have been so other patients didn't see me die. "Can I make a request? Can I go out onto the ward and chat with the other patients" I said.

I went and sat with a lad. I thought I knew him. I realised I'd played football with him. It was over fifty years ago and we remembered each other. Even his scar, which he'd got from one of our players.

Since I've been ill we go to Ibiza. They have a lot of transsexuals there. I might fit in now. They warned me about this because your pectorals get swollen and tender. I'm only joking.

I said to the clinical nurse specialist "I've stopped the pills after seven months, is my hair thicker?" She said it might be but that I might have less body hair. Another side effect might be static electricity, I don't know, but I went to the fridge the other day and I got an electric shock. I've not heard of anyone else having it. I'm seventy-five now. I've always loved my food but now I'm eating cooked tomatoes, sweet potato, root vegetables and red peppers. I'm now so conscious of my diet. I have tomatoes and pumpkin seeds. I chew those – they're good for the prostate.

The surgeons have done their part.

The radiotherapists have done their part.

I'm doing mine. I'll do anything. I don't want it to come back again.

We like to go to Spain for holidays. I spoke to a bloke and we talked about insurance. It's not always easy – insurance, if you're ill abroad. I've said to Sylvia, if anything happens to me abroad well you can leave me up the corner in the hotel room. That would be nice for the next guests!

This week there has been a sparrowhawk out there in the garden near the bird table. There was a big flurry and he was eating another bird. I didn't stop him because he'd go and kill another if I did that. But that's life isn't it?

Looking for Hope

Tajinder's story told by Baksho

"In life we are not trained for the hardest thing,
which is the inevitable."

I can't believe it's nine weeks since the funeral this week; and ten weeks this Wednesday since he died. My daughters and I do talk to each other all the time about their dad but we don't cry in front of each other. I'd like someone for my girls to talk to. At least they've got each other. I worry about my son. He's twenty-eight and he'd started to treat his dad like a friend in the last couple of years.

We've set a date now, the end of March, to take my husband's ashes to India. My son has missed most of his first term at university because of his father's illness.

In life we are not trained for the hardest thing, which is the inevitable.

At the start my thoughts were all jumbled up. I started to make notes of all the things that I wish he'd said and done, that I'd said, my thoughts, things that hurt me. It helps when you write things down. It structures your thoughts. I can't work at the moment. Sometimes I feel angry. We thought we could help him survive cancer. Why didn't God answer our prayers? Why didn't my husband get better?

The start was devastating and went on being devastating.

The Christmas before this last one my husband was experiencing a lot of acid in his stomach. In November the doctor gave him tablets and it seemed to get better. Another doctor gave some antacid tablets but then the condition started again. My husband thought that if both doctors thought it was just acid he must be OK. He left it until July and then asked the doctor to send him to the hospital. There he had a scan. A camera was put inside him. The consultant said that he was 99% sure that he had cancer inside him. He went with my son. They were in shock and decided not to tell us.

One of my daughters was going to study and work in Russia so I said to my husband "I feel there is something you have not told us". "What can I say? I've got cancer" he said. He put his arm around me. "You don't deserve this" I said, and I asked "what happens now?" He said that they were going to send him another appointment for another scan. The next day we had a letter for an appointment in three weeks time.

I went straight up to the surgery. Time was of the essence. He was bad, he was vomiting, and he was feverish. I phoned the hospital. The nurse said that there'd been a cancellation. We went the next day. He could hardly walk. "Dad, how can they send you home you're not well?" my son said.

They said they'd send another appointment in three weeks. So we had to go to the emergency department. He was so weak; he was feverish. My son repeated that he needed to see a doctor straight away. They put my husband on a drip. Twenty minutes later the doctor said " I'm not surprised by the way you felt. You are in shock".

They kept him in over the weekend. They said he could go home on the Monday. "You have a large advanced tumour" the doctor said and he also said he wasn't sure what their options were. Apparently it was so advanced it was blocking his stomach and he could not eat or drink so they needed him to have a bypass operation. I said that we would be very grateful if we could get an appointment for his surgery. I have seven children and they needed their father.

We came home. The hospital gave him a nutrition drink per day because he could not eat or drink. After the bank holiday in August he did not know what to say to us so he did not say a lot, but on the bank holiday he asked the children if they'd like to go out on a day trip. We had both been working. He loved his gardening – that was the way he relaxed.

Anyway, we decided to go to Ludlow Castle for the day. We all went together as a family. You never think this might be the last time we all do this. We took two cars. We had a good day. He was quiet and withdrawn. I don't drive so my son drove one car and my daughter drove the other, it was her friend's car. When we got there she said "Dad, can you help me park it?" It was so endearing. He just did it. It was second nature to him to help her. He was fifty-three and he had driven since he was eighteen.

He was interested in history. He made a point of taking pictures. We tried not to let it enter our heads it might be the last time. I remember him sitting on the grass near the river taking a sip. It was all he could manage.

I was just feeling I needed to be with him. Normally I wouldn't have gone and I'd have got on with some work at home, but from then on I was always with him. I went to all his appointments. The children found out information. They went on the Internet. They researched. We were looking at all the options even spending money. The consultant said "no, it has gone too far". If the doctors had caught it earlier he may have had five more years. That made me bitter. That is something we have to live with.

It seems there is a higher incidence of people with this sort of cancer for Asian and Japanese people. In Japan they have started earlier screening for this.

My husband was always at work; we never had benefits. He would work night and day to bring up seven children. Apart from his gardening he did not know how to deal with the stress. So there were things that could have helped but we did not know that. It's heartache to think it could have been prevented.

He had never been sick before; only colds or flu. He didn't even have high blood pressure. It was such a big shock.

He had the bypass operation. For two weeks he had a little to eat but by the third week he started vomiting. We took him to three or four private doctors. We had an appointment every week with consultants at the hospital. Don't believe everything on the Internet!, they would say. The doctors didn't give us much hope. They did hope that he'd put on weight so that he could go on chemotherapy. In that third week on the Monday and Tuesday we saw two homeopaths. On the Wednesday we saw someone at a specialist clinic about 100 miles away. We were given herbal treatment produced in India and other stuff. The consultant saw my husband. We came back and felt hopeful. Where there is hope, you try.

On the Wednesday coming back from there he was sick. On Thursday he went for mistle-toe treatment. They also gave us hope. He had one injection there. In the car he vomited. In the evening he didn't eat anything. On Friday morning he was vomiting. The doctor at the surgery thought there might be another blockage. She sent him back to the hospital. He was only given sips of water from that time on. He had eaten his last meal. He was dead six weeks later.

For days he went without any treatment. He could not get any rest because he was on a busy ward. When he did go upstairs in the hospital he was told they would do another biopsy to see if they could do another bypass, but the cancer was spreading.

You hope against hope don't you?

They took us into an empty room and told us that the cancer had spread all around the stomach and that there was no more they could do. They said he had days to live not even weeks. My husband didn't want lots of people there. It was always just the children and me. We didn't tell the wider family he had cancer because then you have to deal with them too. We thought we'd tell them after he got better. His own sister and brother knew. The bulk of pain myself and the children took on ourselves. When the doctor gave us the news my daughters phoned their brother. His dad encouraged him to go back because he was missing his study. I plucked up courage to ask the doctor how long he thought my husband had. "Before I answer think about that question. Do you want me to answer that?" he said.

We thought that if we brought him home we'd give it our best to make for him the best we could. We bought in teas and a juicer and aloe vera juice to add to his sips of water. Also, everybody was running around, up and down to the hospital. We thought we should have him at home. The doctors and nurses said that they did not provide drips at home. I kept saying that we wanted him in our own environment. Eventually the Macmillan nurses said they would provide a drip at home. For a whole week he was burning up. On the Saturday night we had to call the doctor in who gave him an injection for his sore throat. On Sunday he was deteriorating more. I asked if it was possible for my husband to go back to hospital and for him to go back on the drip and the doctor said yes. She called for an ambulance.

He went back. After two weeks I asked if we could have the drip at home but for us to do it. I said I would take the responsibility. "Train me and my daughters up," I said. They gave us the training, which was actually only ten or fifteen minutes at the most. We took responsibility for administering it, changing the needle and other actions.

He couldn't walk. I had to help him even to pass water. They gave him a bed here in this living room. They gave him lots of injections. They gave him morphine and we didn't realise. We felt the morphine was taking his life. We had the morphine removed. They seemed to give him any drugs that would remove pain or quicken his death.

I used to sleep on the sofa night and day. He was taking less and less drinks. It was heartbreaking. Visitors would come. It would exhaust him. I would give him a bath. I'd see his bones. I would think, "how is he going to get out of this?" He had wasted away. I kept thinking how I could make him get better out of this. He had always been fit and healthy and good looking too. He always ate fruit and fish a couple of times a week. That's why we can't understand why he had this condition.

Only in the last few weeks it occurred to me that if he had blood when he went to the toilet, he wouldn't have known – he was colour blind. I used to ask him if he'd passed blood and I'd be relieved when he said no. I tell my daughters to pass this information on for if they have sons who might have colour blindness.

My husband was never very communicative. He wouldn't want to talk. He'd brush things off. He told the specialist palliative nurse he wanted counselling for his wife and daughters. He was always a bit religious. We'd sit around the table and he'd say a prayer. He would explain aspects of life to the children and tell them to put their trust in God. He would say God is everywhere. I think he wanted to prepare himself for passing over. He said that just a few weeks before he died. When he found out about his diagnosis he prepared himself by detaching himself from us as a family. We are Sikhs and in an Asian family you detach yourself from this world.

Over the last couple of years he read about other religions and he believed that for us all there is one God.

When the doctors said there were only a couple of days left he talked to the children when I wasn't in the room. "Look after Mum, make sure she eats. Look after yourselves and believe in God" he said. I think he didn't say anything to me because he was preparing himself. He was thinking about us too.

He was never the sort of person to complain. I was always trying to pull him out of that, trying to get him to talk.

I thought all the crying would stop but the tears keep coming. I don't cry in front of the children because it upsets them more. If they want to cry I encourage them. It's OK to cry, I say. I think there are times when they cry quietly to themselves in their rooms and I cry in mine. We try to protect each other. Sometimes I find myself still telling him that even if you don't love us, we love you. I think men can bottle up their emotions.

In fairy tales we are taught to look up to men. In real life it is the other way round.

But it is such a burden now, such a weight because I think I was gliding through life. I knew he was always there. Now when I go on trips I don't panic but I feel the pain of him not being there. He always knew the way; all the back routes. Now I am the one always looking out, I am always alert night and day. Sometimes I think he's looking down at me saying, "now do you know all the things I did?"

My husband had good qualifications. He had an HNC in metallurgy but he worked for the Post Office for twenty-eight years. He liked that there was less responsibility in the job because he said his responsibility was when he came home. He looked after his mother and us. He always did a lot for his wider family. He was greatly loved by my mother and father. He did so much for his extended family and us. He did a lot for everyone. He used to visit his mother every day even if it was for ten minutes. He worked seven days a week if he could get the overtime. "If I wasn't here you'd have a much harder life" he used to say. I remember that now.

Cancer was the last thing we thought my husband would die from. He had had high blood pressure but over the last couple of years that had normalised.

I used to think you could control factors in life. Now I have come to the conclusion that whatever is going to happen will happen. Maybe too much work isn't good for one.

In our culture they say nothing is guaranteed in life but death. It's even more of a burden in our culture – death. People go on and on saying: it's such a loss, you will never get your husband back again, and your children won't have a father. They aren't doing it intentionally to hurt you. There is a period of five weeks in our Asian culture of grieving. Everyone still comes to visit you and it is like they are saying "you will not forget this!" It feels like they are rubbing your face in it. They are saying: "Look how bad it is!" Western culture is more positive. They say there is hope.

Some mornings I don't want to get up out of bed. I'm thinking maybe if I follow my husband I won't feel this pain any more. So I feel bad enough without being told how bad it is over and over again.

If I had to help someone else who had suffered the same as me this is what I would do differently: I would be positive.

When visitors come it is another ritual. I sit and nod my head as they say all these things even though it feels like it's killing me inside. You are already in a corner. I am looking for hope.

When my husband was very ill visitors would come out of duty and my daughters would say "Dad, if you don't feel like seeing anyone pretend you're asleep". That's what helps you if there is someone there to protect you. My husband's belief and hope was that if you suffer here you have a good after life.

"What is it like at the end?" he asked the palliative care nurse. He was preparing himself.

It was important we did our best for him. My husband wanted to be at home at the end. He died in this room. "Mr. Singh, do you want to go home?" the doctors said. My husband turned around and said "you do want to take me home don't you?" "Of course we do Dad" the children replied. We could then spend twenty-four hours with him. We could look after him without having to ask permission for things like in the hospital, or travelling, which wasted time.

Our aim was that we'd make him survive. In Asian culture it's second nature for us to bring him home and look after him. To us it is a privilege.

I would have surmounted any obstacle to make him feel better.

Right at the end my daughter called me from the kitchen. "Dad's trying to say something" she said. I couldn't understand him. I was still holding his hands when he died. "You can't leave us, you can't leave your daughters" I was saying. Perhaps I could have given him artificial resuscitation.

A Kind of Journey

Angela's Story

"I'm going to fight as much as I can fight in order to preserve my life for as long as I can."

My sister took it worse than I did. "Why couldn't it be me?" she said. "I wouldn't want it to be you, or anyone else because at the end of the day whatever kind of journey I have to go on I wouldn't want to push it onto anybody else" I said. Even though I am the younger sister I am the stronger one. I had to be her comforter. Don't worry I'm not going anywhere and God willing I will get through this, I had to say. We had to switch roles. My sister and me are very close. I think for her it was the initial shock of, oh no my sister's got cancer. It did shake her up. Even now she fusses over me but she said it has made her stronger. She says I have instilled strength in her. If I hadn't then maybe it would be hard to cope with myself and with my sister. I'm trying to show her that if she gets stressed out then she may end up in my predicament.

When I was diagnosed the doctor said I wasn't going to die. What do we do next? was my main thought. I was diagnosed in 2003. At the time I was having tests for my heart because I suffer with high blood pressure and I was getting palpitations. I remember having a bath and thinking that I was going to have to have a pacemaker. I'd not had an operation besides having caesarean section with my children. How am I going to cope? I was thinking. My daughter came into my room after I'd had a bath and I have always checked myself, I've always done it. "Mom, what are you doing that for?" she asked. I explained and while she was talking to me she said, "Mom, you've got a lump on your breast". I had been thinking about the pacemaker, but she was right you could actually see it and I could feel it.

She encouraged me to go to the doctor. I had to go and see the doctor anyway. My doctor was very good. "I'm going to get you checked out at the hospital" she said. The thought crossed my mind that this could be serious. However, what took away a lot of my fear was the thought of the pacemaker. I was so focused on that. I had the mammogram very quickly. I went with my mom.

I was struck by how many people were in the waiting room. All these people of all different ages diagnosed with cancer, and people kept coming up to my mom. "How are you coping?" they'd say. They were presuming it was her not me. "It's not me it's my daughter" she'd say.

When the doctor called me in I didn't even sit down. "Is it cancer?" I asked. He couldn't hide it he said, "I'm so sorry," and at that point I wanted to say, "it's alright" but then my thoughts switched to my mom who was in reception and I began to wonder how I was going to tell her. So I asked how bad it was and if I was going to die. He said he wasn't sure and that I needed to have a biopsy. I just wanted to know yes or no, and I had to go back the next day. They said they weren't sure but that I might have to have a mastectomy.

I had to get a Macmillan nurse to tell my mom. She knew from my expression. I'd said I didn't want my mom to be in the room with me because I thought it would be too hard for her. My main concern at the time was for my mom because she'd lost my father and was still recovering from that. I had said to her before I went in that it could be cancer or it could be a cyst because a lot of people had said that. At the same time at the back of my mind I had to be prepared and get my head together. I asked my Macmillan nurse to explain to my mom because I didn't think I'd be able to use the words in the right order. I asked her to explain it for me. I remember my mom looking at me and me saying, "I need you to speak to my Macmillan nurse". My mom didn't say a word she just held my hand and squeezed it so I knew. "Don't worry if it's bad news I'm here" she said. When the nurse explained I didn't look at my mom because I thought that if I looked at her she might break down. That to me would have been hard, you know. "Are you alright?" I kept saying and she was saying to me "are you alright?" It can't be easy for you to hear your child has been diagnosed with cancer, which people generally associate with older people.

The nurse explained things but I couldn't take it all in. Later I had to ask my mom "did she say such and such, because I can't remember?" All that kept going through my mind at that point was that I was going to die and I said to my mom, "I have got my two daughters to look after". I said to the doctor I wanted to know and I said "I know you're not God but I just want to know what are my chances?" "Will she have to have chemo?" my mom was saying. It was that that really shook my mom. I remember the expression on her face.

About a week later (it was very quick) I had to go on chemo because they said the cancer had progressed. I had chemo before I actually had my operation to shrink the lump because it was a good size. It was still growing. So after I had my chemo I had a lumpectomy.

What helped me be strong was that from my first diagnosis I met people who were willing to explain. I was in my late thirties and from a black person's point of view there weren't many people who you could talk to and ask about their experience and what kind of things I could expect. I would like other people who perhaps are the same age group as me or ethnic background to know this is how I dealt with it. When I had my mastectomy I could imagine what I would look like but none of the books showed it from the perspective of a black or Asian person. That's how Kay came into it. She was a patient too and we became friends. I could explain to her what it was like having chemo and she could explain to me what it was like having reconstruction. At the moment I haven't had reconstruction.

I remember it was amazing being diagnosed because suddenly everywhere I looked seemed to be about breast cancer – there was that woman on Holby City. I remember her saying that for women who might fear having this operation this is how you'll look. She was the first person who I saw physically and I thought – it doesn't look that bad. I also thought, how am I going to look? My scar's going to look totally different to that because she's a different colour. On GMTV that particular week they explained how you look before and how you can look after. It gave me a bit of peace of mind. It was very helpful.

In 2003 I had the chemo from July to the January. About March I went for my first surgery, that was the lumpectomy. The consultant said that because of my age he didn't want to do a mastectomy, but I ended up with a blood clot. I went through quite a rough time. My consultant was fantastic but the person who worked under her just didn't listen. I asked if he could tell me anything I should look out for so I could identify good or bad. I kept getting very dizzy. My drain seemed to be filling up with a lot of blood. It eased up but then it started getting kind of swollen et cetera. That gave me a bit of a problem so I got that done and then after that got the results back. They said it had progressed even further so therefore I would have to have the mastectomy. I chose to have that straight away. Two months after having the lumpectomy I was back in surgery having the mastectomy. They said that hopefully they had got everything.

The night before surgery I had a bath and I remember talking to my breast and saying "I'm going to miss you so much but it is something that has to be done and if it means saving my life it will have to be done".

I can have reconstruction if I want to but in a way I wish I could have had it while having the surgery, but that wasn't to be for me.

I think my biggest knock was when after I had my lumpectomy I had to go back to see my consultant for my results, and I'll never forget I was sitting in the room and I knew it was bad news. I suspected it because so many of them came into the room. "Why are so many people coming into this room?" I thought. There was my surgeon, my Macmillan nurse, and another nurse that I had been talking to. In all there were four people and I sensed they'd say that I would have to go down the mastectomy route. I started to rock because I was so nervous. I was wondering what was going on and I was a bit agitated. When they came in I got jittery. My mom rubbed my hands as though to say, you'll be all right.

My consultant knew I was a friendly kind of person who gets on with people but she could see what I was going through. "Just tell me what's going on!" I said and I started getting into a panic. "Why do you need so many people in this room? Why do you need so many people to tell me?" "You'll be alright. Come on, Angie, calm down now" my mom said. My head was spinning but I knew I did need to calm down because I knew that whatever it was she was going to tell me I wouldn't take it in if I didn't. It brought back memories of when I had my youngest daughter and I had to have an emergency Caesarean and I can remember just seeing all these people. So I thought – this is going to be bad news. As the consultant talked I had to look at my mom because I couldn't take it in and I wanted my mom to. It was reality and I knew that what she explained to me wasn't going to go away. I kept saying "am I going to lose my breast?" and my mom was asking if I'd need chemotherapy. The answer was yes, but I honestly can't remember a lot of it. "Right, what are we going to do and what will the treatment be like?" I began to think once I calmed down.

By the time I started on chemo I had peace of mind that I knew that they had done everything possible to prevent me from having a mastectomy and dealing with it that way. I could say, well they tried the lumpectomy and that couldn't stop what was happening now.

When I had my first course of chemo my nurse explained everything. If I was worried about anything she'd tell me the truth. I said I didn't want to be pampered. I said that if anything was going to hurt me to tell me so that I could prepare myself. I needed to come to terms with the experience and understand it so that I could deal with it.

The nurse explained to me that with the chemo my hair was going to go. She told me of other side effects too so from that first session I could prepare myself. I didn't want to wear the hospital wigs because they looked too bulky and didn't look natural so I had my own wigs made. They are caps and they consist of human hair. They made me feel more in control, better. I could have the styles that I wanted.

On my first course of chemo my mom came with me and my doctor organised for an ambulance to pick me up. "Do you need a wheelchair?" they would say approaching my mom.

I've always said I don't want people feeling sorry for me. As soon as the word cancer is mentioned I don't want them to think, poor Angie. I want them to think I am the same person. I have high blood pressure and I have to take medication for that, with cancer it's just the same. I have to have treatment.

The chemo went fine but I gained a lot of weight. I went from eleven stone to sixteen stone. That was the steroids. My doctor said that if I had not had that operation when I did I wouldn't have lived to see Christmas. I didn't know that at the time because I left it up to my doctor how to tell me and to judge the timing of that. She told me things, but not all at once. After my operation and after my chemo I was more focused. I just got on with it. That was my way of dealing with it, because of my family and my friends I couldn't think, well it should have been you. I thought God willing I've got a chance here. I'm going to fight as much as I can fight in order to preserve my life for as long as I can.

Some days having the chemo made me very tired. I had days when I was up and I was down. I don't know whether it was an adrenaline thing but most of my times were up. Last year though was a very bad year for me. I don't know whether the reality of what I had actually been through hit me. A lot of it was to do with my last operation. Physically and mentally I had to go inside myself to bring myself out of it because when I was diagnosed with cancer it didn't seem to affect me as much as when I had the operation – the symptoms and the emotions. I think also the medication; I was on morphine and that had a lot to do with bringing me down. I think it was just the fact of the reality – this is what my body has been through. Also financially it was difficult. Before being diagnosed I was working. I was planning to train to teach. I had just qualified as a chef and cake decorator and I wanted to go out into the community to give it back. That is not possible right now. Another thing was I found last year my daughter was diagnosed with diabetes at sixteen.

Financially, with state benefit, they give it you today and tomorrow they take it away from you and I found, therefore, I was having problems with my finances. If I had to go somewhere I would have to pay for taxis et cetera and I found that it hit me then and took me to a very dark place. I found that if you can cope with it they tend not to be there.

The Bridges Care Coordinator recommended the massage therapy that was absolutely the best.

"Do you know what, I'm just going to book it" my sister said to me one day. She booked a holiday in Turkey. That was absolutely amazing. Everything I'd been through all this time hit me – I was crying. I couldn't eat, couldn't sleep, I was snappy. The medication was affecting me. Also the menopause - I was having hot flushes. My body was aching and that made me very low. If other people said, "I've been through all of this and it hasn't affected me" I'd have to think - really? I've met ladies in hospital who've been having breakdowns because they can't cope with it. It hit me and when it did I felt relieved in a way. I can't be high energy all the time.

God is on my side. My faith in God has got stronger and I've met amazing people. One woman had a double mastectomy and another had cancer through her body and she was like a skeleton. She was posh, and we would have a laugh and a joke. We'd talk and she'd tell me certain things. The nurses found it hard to talk to her because she'd say she didn't want to talk. I remember saying I was going to have a makeover and I told her that when I did I would come and show her – you know, just to pick her up. " Yes, I would like that" she said. I phoned up and went to the hospital and when I got to the ward the nurse asked me to come to the side. She had just passed away. She had twins, eighteen months old.

The other lady I met was when I went for my mastectomy. This lady was a teacher. I remember she was walking around and then as the days progressed she couldn't get out of bed. We used to talk at night time. You've got to fight it we used to say to her. I heard her take her last breath. When I do have my low days I think of them. I know they would like to be in my position. I use that as my strength to pick myself back up.

I was at hospital last week and I met this gentleman. This lady sat next to me and I told her I'd come for a check-up and I said if you like I'll explain what happened to me. In my family I say check yourself. I tell them what a mastectomy looks like. I find that people explained certain things and that made me feel comfortable. When I go to the hospital they sometimes ask if I will have a trainee. I say yeah because if they don't learn we aren't going to survive. I want to survive as long as I can. I have no qualms in explaining to other people. I explained to this lady's husband, who was quite agitated, she will have to go through chemo. "Do you feel like you're getting to that light at the end of the tunnel?" he said. "Do you know something, I try not to think about that tunnel I just concentrate on what is happening now" I replied.

Hopefully I will progress to the end of the tunnel but at this point in time I have come to my fifth year. If I dwell on the end of the tunnel it will start making me feel paranoid. His partner said to me that she felt that there was light at the end of the tunnel. Hopefully I am getting closer to getting there but I also have to be realistic and I know that it can come back. Therefore I have to think, don't think about the light just concentrate on now. We could all walk outside and get knocked down by a bus. Positivity has got me to the point that I have got to now. I reached that low point. Now I go with the flow and I'll deal with it in the best way I can.

People say to me, has it changed you? In some ways it has but I am still the same person I was. If anything it has made me a bit stronger. My friends say that I do too much for people rather than for myself. Sometimes now I also do things for me.

Finances aren't there. Being at my low point I thought, survive on what you've got. Why are you worried because if you're dead tomorrow they can't be paid. Last year I wouldn't have been able to talk to you like this. In certain ways it has made me stronger.

When I come out of this life there will be some one else in the same predicament and so by sharing my story I hope to help them.

In 2004 I had my second operation I didn't have to have chemo after that.

I did have a lot of problems when I was in hospital after my surgery. They thought they saw a shadow over my ovary but luckily enough it wasn't anything serious. It caused a lot of pain. I was in hospital for a month. The pain was horrific and it was worse than anything else. That's why I haven't been in for reconstruction.

During the chemo I drank a lot of water and tried to stay positive and also my cousin in London used to phone me up and send me CDs. That really helped. "If Mummy is by herself it doesn't mean I don't love you; I just need to be by myself" I would say to my daughters.

Regarding my children, my eldest is now nineteen and my youngest is fourteen. It was my eldest who saw the lump. I decided from the beginning I would tell them the truth and I waited to get all the information before I did that. My eldest went on the Internet. "Mummy, if you have to have chemo, it's not as bad as it used to be" she said.

I remember having my chemo. I had my hair in extension plaits. At the hospital they said, "Oh you've got such beautiful hair and you're going to lose it all". "When I come back again I'll come back different" I said. So when I went home I washed it and the one thing I didn't want was to lie down and it to come off on the pillow. As I tried to make plaits it began to fall out. My youngest daughter said, "I don't know how to tell you this, Mom, be prepared ... Your hair's coming out". It had started to come out at the root. "I don't want you to do it by yourself. So I'll feel better if I can help" she said. So I remember taking it out... I was completely bald then. "Come on you can help me wash it" I said to her and that was my way for her not to be scared.

My older daughter had been out and I remember going to the door and my younger daughter said, "be strong now, because Mom's lost all her hair". For about two hours she couldn't come into the room. Eventually she composed herself. I put a headscarf on. "I want to see what you look like because I want you to be able to walk around the house comfortable" she said. I made a promise that if I did lose my hair I wouldn't cut it. Having the wig on you're not going to be able to see it any way.

I have to give credit to the women who walk around without the scarves and a bald head. It's not a vanity thing from me. I just didn't feel comfortable except in my own house. With my youngest nephew I was careful because his parents died from cancer. He said to me "it breaks my heart". So I had a code. "Fix up, look sharp" he'd say, so therefore, I'd know to fix it. With my other nephew he was different. "What do you think about my new hairstyle?" I'd say to him and he'd go, "there you go again". But that was my way for them to feel comfortable around me. I didn't want them to tiptoe around me.

One day I had like a premonition just before I was diagnosed. What would I do if I had cancer? I thought. I was watching telly and the thought of cancer came into my head. My mom thinks it was a way I could be prepared.

I refuse to let it beat me. I am also realistic that there is a possibility it can come back, but we can get through it if we have to. I had an aunty who died from it. It gives me the strength to say, come on now, pick yourself up, brush yourself down and fight this. Some friends have distanced themselves. "Look, if I'm not feeling good on a particular day then I will just tell you" I've said.

I went on holiday. I wore a bikini. I had put on weight and I'd always been kind of slim but it was what was keeping me alive. I say don't feel sorry for yourself because I've seen the children and babies on the wards in hospital. They have to put them to sleep to give them the chemo. That makes me say to myself, I'm awake. It takes some things like that to take you out of yourself.

Shining

Kay's Story

*"I sing a lot wherever I may be
to keep my mind free and happy"*

My name is Kay-Dionne. I was diagnosed with cancer at the age of thirty in 2003. I was terrified when I found out I had breast cancer. The first thing I thought was that I was going to die and I wouldn't see my children grow up.

People were shocked when I told them I had breast cancer. Some said I looked so well.

At this moment in time I'm studying at college for a childcare diploma. My aim is to run my own nursery.

I have three children: Rahkeem, aged ten; Raheesha, aged nine; and Rasheka, aged five. I was breast-feeding Rasheka, who was two months old at the time, when I felt a lump in my breast. It was as hard as a rock. My GP referred me to a consultant. That's how I found out it was cancer. It was a huge shock. I was on my own when I was diagnosed. I felt like the world was spinning. I was really worried about my little ones. I thought, I'm not going to see my little ones grow up.

Three months later I had a mastectomy and a reconstruction. After, I had six months of chemo and three weeks of radiotherapy. My kids had to go into care because my family couldn't have them. I was in a domestic violence refuge. My kids went into care for a year and a half. That was until I finished treatment. It was very depressing because I was going through the treatment and I missed the kids. It was so hard to cope with things some times. My breast care nurse referred me to a lady that was diagnosed with cancer and she was the one who helped me in the breast unit to talk about things. She was about five years ahead of me in terms of the illness and I could phone her any time and get upset or anything like that. It helps knowing another person who has gone through it. It's much easier to relate to someone who has been through that process. We still keep in touch.

I also got a lot of information by reading through leaflets that talked about what cancer is and the treatments. That really helped a lot, as did talking to other people, other ladies I met. With the help of my breast care nurse and a leaflet I got from the unit I sat my children down one evening and I said to them that I had cancer and that I was going through the process of treatment. I told them what to expect like my hair falling out. I told them so that if they saw me looking different they would know what that change was. They did cope with it but my son didn't cope too well at the time. The first girl was really aggressive in school and my son's schoolwork fell down because he was thinking about it a lot. He cried a lot while he was in care. Sometimes they would phone me up so that I would speak to him before he went to sleep. At the time Rahkeem was about six or seven and Rash was in nursery; the youngest was too young to know.

The refuge was very supportive. I finished all my treatment in the refuge. I did get to see my kids regularly. I had a social worker and the foster carers were so good and said that I could come any time to see them. That was a great relief. The kids were separated but they were living with two sisters on the same road. The two eldest were together and the baby was with the other sister.

When my chemo doctor told me that I was going to lose my hair I went to the hairdressers and had it all shaved off. It made me feel better to know I'd done it all myself rather than see my hair fall out bit by bit. I'm on Tamoxifen for five years. The chemo and the radiotherapy all happened in the same year – 2004.

My reconstruction the following year was hurtful and the implant was moving around my body. I told my plastic surgeon. If I laid down the implant was coming up my chest and if I was walking I could feel it moving around.

Living with cancer is frightening but I have to be strong. No matter what anyone says I have to keep fighting instead of letting my fear run away with me. I have done my best to stay positive and keep my mind strong. I am determined to beat cancer because of my children. Whenever I looked at their faces and saw fear and pain I told myself to never give up. I want to die trying. I am a member of the Black Minority Ethnic Cancer, which offers support and promotes awareness. I feel all right now; I feel bright. I'm shining because having been through this process and having got back my kids I feel now I have to prove myself. Now I just have to move forward.

I still go back for my check-ups. I went for a mammogram last year and that was clear. I have also had tests for cancer in the womb but I don't get my results until the 28th of this month. After that I will know what's happening. That's because my smear tests kept coming back abnormal. That's why they had to take tissues from my womb. In a way it's depressing because I am trying to move on and this feels like it's holding me back. I keep trying to think positive and I just want to hear positive things.

When I was diagnosed with cancer I didn't think, this is it. Although at the beginning I did think about death. It kept coming to my mind and I thought, I'm going to die, I'm going to die, what am I going to do? Then I thought about the kids. I couldn't just think about myself. What is going to happen to them if something happens to me? I thought. That really helped because I knew I had to be strong for them. Going through my process of treatment I would never let them see me crying or looking depressed. I always made it look as if everything was OK. I didn't want them to go away depressed.

I have a support group now and we find time for each other and phone each other. We are planning our first event, which is a picnic in the park, everyone will be invited to come and bring along a game and play.

I'm with a new partner who is supportive. With the children and when I'm in hospital he is always there and supporting me. I also get support from the breast unit and Bridges. They are very helpful. I do a lot of voluntary work for breast cancer. This year I intend to do a run. That's in Sutton Park.

To anyone who is living with cancer I would offer these words of encouragement: be strong, think positive, and keep smiling. Whenever I feel down my children, partner, mum and friends give me words of encouragement. I sing a lot wherever I may be to keep my mind free and happy.

I think another person's story will uplift the person hearing it. It can help. Not everyone gets the support that they should get because family or friends don't really know what they are going through.

I was afraid to let my mum know that I had cancer and it was my brother who told her because I know how depressing that can be. My brother and mother are both back home in Jamaica, so it is difficult having that distance. I miss them a lot. We send photos and we speak a lot on the phone. I do have family here but they all live in London.

My name is Rahkeem and I am ten years old. When I found out my mom had cancer I was sad but now that she got the test I feel much happier.

My name is Raheesha and I am eight years old. When I found out my mom had cancer we went in child care. I felt worried because I thought something was going to happen. Now I feel much better because my mom made a big progress.

My name is Fred and I am Kay's partner. When I first met her I never thought of her as a cancer patient. She is always doing something and never feeling sorry for herself. I always try my best to support her because she is a very independent person and most of all she doesn't like pity. My words of encouragement are: be positive, think of the future and most of all be happy with who you are.

Acknowledgements

In projects of this kind it is often the case that the idea, or ideas, for such work come from a variety of sources that coalesce or combine at a collective point. All are then needed to move forward in a particular direction. This was definitely the case here! I write this as the End of Life Care Lead at Strategic Health Authority (SHA) NHS West Midlands. I would like to acknowledge and thank enormously the following contributors:

Liz Cadogan, who until April 2007 was the Arts in Health Lead at the SHA. It is through my conversations with her about how we could use arts in and for addressing end of life care issues in training and to develop stories for supporting individuals that led to an unfolding process for this piece of work. This culminated in an application to the Arts Council for some funding. This process took over a year, but Liz's enthusiasm and expertise in the artists' world and support for the proposal process was just great.

Alongside this Manjula Patel, Manager of Bridges Support service, and myself were members of a national group, 'Wellbeing in Dying', where we were exploring some practical steps that might improve end of life care experiences. Manjula raised issues about the small number of 'voices' and 'stories' from the public that were available to or accessible by all members of the public.

Bridges, as stated in the preface, are committed to the use of narrative as their underpinning way of working with their clients, so it was not surprising that Bridges would be keen to be major players in this piece of work. And of course Manjula's input to this piece of work has been a shining light and we really could not have achieved what we have without her dedication to this cause of people's stories being heard and shared.

Manjula thanks the Bridges and Sandwell Hospice at Home teams for helping to recruit the participants to the project and Jennifer and Michelle for transcribing the tapes.

Through Liz, and with Manjula, we then employed Maria Whatton as our professional storyteller and so began the work as the project team to undertake this very new and, we think, quite innovative way of approaching the development of a community story for and about end of life.

Maria has been a delight. Her knowledge of stories, their roots, how to use them, tell them and how to generate a new one fit for our experiences in the twenty-first century is truly wonderful.

Maria then brought the expertise of Anne Kinnaird into the story collecting and formatting process. Anne is another professional artist who works in a range of media. So Anne brought another dimension to our work. Her eagerness to be part of the work, her interest in and support of the work made her a very welcome team member.

Then of course many thanks to Jovian Productions, the arts production company that took our idea and work and translated this into the book you now have.

As for funding support I would like to thank NHS West Midlands, the Arts Council, Bridges Support and Pan Birmingham Palliative Care Network
(See www.birminghampalliativecare.nhs.uk)

And finally, last but not least, enormous thanks to the participants who we have thanked in various ways in the introduction to this book. Thank you Gill Reed, Barbara Pardon, Dot Short, Sheila Spencer, Babs Panton, Bob Bloomer, Doreen Keeling, Angela Thompson, Kay Green and Baksho Johal.

Life, living and dying really is something we all share!

Pauline Smith
End of Life Care Lead NHS West Midlands